Springtime's PROMISE

by
Carrie Bender

Springtime's Promise

Library of Congress Number: 2009927076
International Standard Book Number: 978-1-60126-180-9

Printed 2009 by
Masthof Press
219 Mill Road
Morgantown, PA 19543-9516

This book is fiction.
Some parts are based on actual happenings,
but not always at the correct time
in which they occurred.

Table of Contents

PART ONE

Springtime

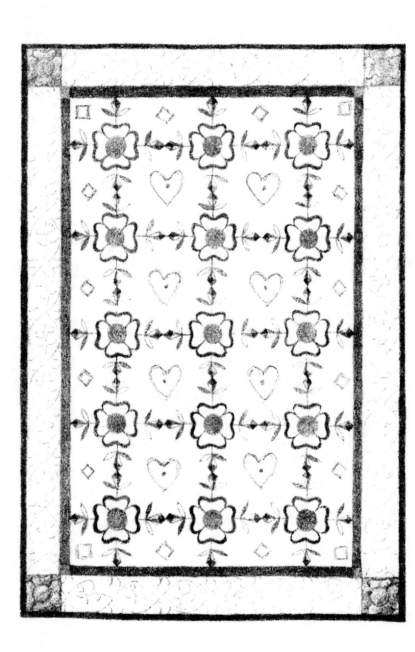

My New Home

Today, March 31st, is my birthday and I can still hardly believe that I'm really here at my dear wonderful grandparents' place at last. This past winter seemed to last forever. I don't believe I could have endured it had it not been for the promise of springtime. Now springtime's promise is fulfilled, and I am so joyous and thankful to be here. Throughout the long, dreary winter I was looking forward to this time, and it is every bit as wonderful as I dreamed it would be—a bit of heaven on earth.

I wish I were more of a writer and could put my thoughts on paper better, for I want to write about every member of this family—my dear grandmother whom I call Mumsy, and grandfather whom I call Grandpap and all the aunts and uncles. Both Mumsy and Grandpap seem too young to be grandparents. They still have 7 of their 14 children at home yet, from 23-year-old Caleb down to 12-year-old Jonathan. It seems strange to have an uncle younger than myself, and one just a year older than myself, but so it is. And then, there are the seven married ones and all their little ones.

My dad was the oldest. He married a girl from Ohio, who was my mother Hannah. She died of tuberculosis when I was only four years old.

Dad and I lived alone until last fall when he died from typhoid fever. When he knew that his time here on earth was short, he arranged for me to travel with friends of his to Lancaster County, Pennsylvania, to live with my grandparents. It didn't suit them to start out until spring, so I had to spend the winter with Aunt Hepsi. (She really isn't my aunt, but for some reason everyone calls her Aunt Hepsi.)

It was lonely and boring there, and that's why I looked forward to springtime so much. The grief of losing Dad was made bearable by my cherished plans for spring. I knew what it was like at Mumsy's house, because Dad and I made a trip to Pennsylvania when I was eight years old, and I spent two wonderful weeks with them then. That memory, along with all the stories Dad told me about his old home, parents, brothers and sisters, made me long to be with them the rest of my life.

I wasn't one bit disappointed; they're still as loving and caring and as lively and jolly as I remembered them to be, and being here is a dream come true. Ya well, it's time to quit my scribbles for now, for the girls are making taffy and it's time to pull it into long strands. I'll write more about my new family and my birthday later.

BY THE OLD MILL

I'm sitting here beside the little bridge that spans the mill-race. From here I can hear the murmur of the water as it flows down over the dam in the run. The run flows into the Conestoga Creek, and that flows westward on out to the mighty Susquehanna River.

I love the sound of the mill drawing water, the waters over the dam, the frogs' throaty croaking in the *schwamm* (swamp), and the joyous singing of the birds.

Today feels as warm as summer, which is unusual for this early in April, Mumsy says. The warm breezes are laden with the sweet scents of springtime—green things pushing through the rich earth, and just the fragrance of springtime itself. In contrast, I remember one day last November when I was so lonely, homesick and sad. Aunt Hepsi had been extra hard to bear that day, and

I just had to get outside. I went for a walk back a field lane along the woods nearby, and had a good cry.

I was wondering if God was really there and really cared about people's heartaches and had a plan for everyone, or if He was a remote God that had too many other things to take care of. I prayed, "O God, if you hear my prayer and really care, then let the clouds part right now and the sun shine through." (It was a very overcast day with leaden skies hanging low.)

Well, nothing happened, and I felt more discouraged than ever. I cried some more as I slowly headed back to the house. Aunt Hepsi must have noticed traces of tears, and pried out of me why I was crying. Then she scolded me for seeking a sign. She said in the Bible it says that it's a wicked generation that seeks after a sign, it is strictly forbidden, and that God wants us to believe in Him and trust Him without a sign of our own choosing.

Maybe I shouldn't have written that Aunt Hepsi was hard to bear; she probably was one of those that are "the salt of the earth," but she watched over me with an eagle eye, and was a bit salty about it, which made me feel nigh to suffocation. Her spiel was, "Don't go outside without your overshoes, don't sit near a drafty window," and "Did you have your window open a bit last night again?" "Do you have your long pettipants on," and "Don't forget your ear cap," etc., etc.

I partly blamed it on Dad's doctor. He had told her there's a possibility that I would become consumptive like my mother. I guess she felt responsible for my health, and didn't realize how much I chafed under her over-protectiveness.

I think Aunt Hepsi was even a bit triumphant when in February I got a cough I just couldn't shake, and a pain in the right side of my chest. (Oh, but I didn't tell her about the pain in my chest; she would have for sure made me stay in bed. I still feel it

every now and then, but my cough is better—a cause for rejoicing.)

Now, to finish my story . . . A few weeks later, on a day that was just as dreary and cloudy, I was again walking back through Aunt Hepsi's field lane and stopped under that same tree where I had asked God to let His sun shine through the clouds. I leaned against the rough bark of the tree thinking gloomily about my lonely, dreary existence. Then, to my amazement, the clouds parted and the sun shone through for awhile. I felt greatly cheered, for I felt sure that God was there and that He cared, and I would get through the winter somehow and that spring would eventually arrive.

Oh dear, now Naomi is calling me and I haven't written anything about my new family members (young aunts and uncles) yet. That will have to wait until next time.

BY THE LITTLE BRIDGE

The weather is as summer-like as it was the last time I came down here in spite of Grandpap's prediction that we could soon have chilly weather again. A song sparrow is sweetly trilling from the bushes, clumps of wild flowers are blooming, and tendrils of wild ferns are poking through the earth at my feet. A moment ago, I saw a colorful ring-necked pheasant strutting by with his hen.

Yesterday I made the mistake of telling Mumsy about the pain in my chest that won't quite go away. She looked alarmed and hustled me off to the doctor. I think she was secretly afraid I was coming down with tuberculosis, but thankfully, the doctor didn't seem alarmed. He said I'm not consumptive (yet), but that I'll have to be careful and not over-exert myself, nor let myself get rundown. He said to Mumsy, "Let her keep to the open air and sunshine as much as possible. The great outdoors will be good for her this summer." Oh, I sure was glad to hear that, for I was fearing I'd be kept indoors stitching quilts, hooking rugs, knitting, and other boring stuff.

Now that I am here by the bridge, maybe I can finally write about my dear ones. (If a horse and wagon goes by on the mill road, I'll just slip behind the bushes by the millrace until they're past.) I don't know many people in this area yet. I'm thankful that not many people have automobiles out here in the rural areas yet like they do in the cities.

I'll start with Mumsy—she's a kind, pleasant-faced, round-cheeked motherly woman. Her large white prayer *kapp* covers most of her still dark and wavy hair, and kindness and friendliness shine out of her warm gray eyes. Grandpap—is tall and strong and has twinkling eyes. He likes to tease a bit, in a friendly way. My dad looked a lot like him and had the same chuckle.

The married ones are Joel (my dad), Elizabeth, Katie, Rachel, Lydia, Jacob and Lovina. At home yet are Caleb, 23; Barbara, 21; Maria, 20; Susanna, 18; Naomi 16; Steven 14; and Jonathan 12. Caleb, Barbara and Maria are spoken for (so to speak). They're keeping company—young men come calling on Sunday evenings, and Caleb goes somewhere else.

Susanna is the beauty of the family and Naomi has the most outgoing personality. Steven and Jonathan are full of good-natured fun. They aren't past the prank playing stage, and they probably think their aunt is fair game. I hope I'm not an unsuspecting victim.

I had never really known what it was like to be part of a big family until I came here. I loved my dad, and yet he could not have realized how lonely I felt sometimes. Mumsy already seems like a real mother to me, and my aunts like my older sisters. This big, rambling farmhouse seems like home—a real home filled with love, peace and harmony. This seems to be a big farm with many acres of beautiful farmland, grassy wood pastures, orchards, and the meadowlands beyond the mill.

Grandpap and the boys are plowing these days—walking behind the hand plow, turning over the long furrows of rich, dark earth. The girls are busy with the spring housecleaning, and I'm helping and learning. They're always singing and bantering, talking and teasing good-naturedly. I'm only beginning to realize what I've been missing all these years. For example, I had never had anyone make a fuss over me on any of my birthdays until I was here. The girls sang "Happy Birthday" and pulled my ears and Maria made a cake for me, all frosted and decorated with pecans. They gave me this journal and a brush and comb set, and in the evening we made taffy. To think that I almost missed being part of a big, happy family!!

Some might think it strange that I use Carpenter for my last name, when Dad and Grandpap's family use Zimmerman. It's because my mother preferred the English version of the name. Dad said I should keep it that way now, for Mother's sake, and so I will, even though I'd prefer Zimmerman.

There goes Steven with his fishing line, with Patsy the dog trailing after him, sniffing out the bunnies' trails. I think I'll go join them.

BY THE DAM

I'm sitting here on the rock ledge above the dam, fascinated by the water tumbling down over and continuing on and on. To think that this same creek was here when the Indians roamed the Conestoga Valley. I wonder how all the creeks and rivers got their names. Jonathan told me he knows how the Cocalico got its name—it was named *Hoch Halekung* by the Indians (*Hoch Halekung* in the Indian language means "den of snakes"), because snakes were plentiful in that area. If you say *Hoch Halekung* fast, it sounds like Cocalico, so that's what it became. I've heard that the Conestoga Valley was the most fertile and well watered in all of Penn's woods.

Grandpap often tells stories about the long-ago days, in the evenings, when supper is over. He leans back in his chair and we (especially me) listen spellbound. I think I'll write some of the happenings he relates here in my journal so I remember them to tell to my children and grandchildren, if I ever have any.

Long ago, when Grandfather brought his bride to this farm, gypsies still came through the area regularly. The colorfully dressed wanderers asked to camp down in the meadow by the mill. These gypsies were not only skilled, but shrewd in business and did more than earn their bread. They came to the door selling baskets, brooms, and other things they had made. Some claimed to be fortune-tellers, and those who agreed to have their fortune revealed, would later find out that their money or watch was missing. They traded horses too, and craftily were able to trade a poor horse for a good one. Lots of little children played around their wagons and kettles of stew simmered over their fires. In the evenings the adults sang and danced and played musical instruments.

Road walkers, or tramps, were common in the area, too. They walked the roads, stopping at farmhouses along the way for their meals. They marked the telephone poles, letting the other tramps know which were the good places—good meals and good measure. They asked to sleep on the hay in the farmers' barns, handing over their matches until the next morning when they came to the house for breakfast, and then on the road again. When the weather was bad they would gather in the horse shed at Weaverland Church. They had another hangout in a hollow in the Turkey Hill area, where they sat around a campfire and boiled their strong coffee, probably visiting and telling stories.

The Negroes came down from the Welsh Mountains, asking for ear corn and hay for their horses. Once, one tied his undernourished horse at the mailbox. Just as he was heading back to the wagon with his armload of corn they gave him, the horse got himself loose and started trotting down the road, heading for home without him. The man ran after him, but would not drop his armload of corn in order to run faster. If someone else had not caught the horse for him, he would have had to walk all the way home, carrying his corn. A one-legged Negro woman regularly came in a buggy with her bottle-drinking baby on her lap. They often asked for ham or a piece of *speck*, but usually had to be satisfied with potatoes, turnips and corn, for if a farmer gave them too much, they'd come back all the sooner asking for more. Once a plump lady helped herself to a ham from the smokehouse, smuggling it out under her skirt. The hired man saw her and tried to make her put it back. She had a little girl along and hollered for her to throw stones at him, but he did manage to take the ham from her.

Another time when a family of Negroes asked for ham, Grandfather told them that his hams spoiled for him this year and he buried them. They begged him to tell them where he buried the hams. Finally he allowed them to dig them up. They were very happy to have found such a prize, and thanked him over and over. Next time they came around he asked them, "How were the hams?"

"Good, good," was their reply. "All we had to do was cook them in soda water and that took the taint right out."

Another time a Negro lady came in a buggy. Just as she was stepping into the buggy to leave, her horse made a lunge, throwing her down. Her foot got caught somehow, and the horse ran off dragging her along quite a ways until someone caught him. She was injured and Grandfather carried her to the house and they put her to bed in the *commar* (downstairs bedroom) for a week until she was able to drive home again.

Ya well, twilight is descending and I must go inside before it gets damp and Mumsy must scold me. She's not half as bad as Aunt Hepsi was for being over-protective—she says I'm old enough to take care of myself, and I guess I am, too.

Oh, oh, just now a flock of wild geese landed in the reeds in the swampy area in back of the mill. They are so beautiful, almost majestic. I wish I could watch them longer.

SUNDAY SERVICES

We went to church at Weaverland this forenoon and heard an inspiring sermon. A visitor was there who didn't understand German, so they had part of the sermon in English—something they would not have done back home.

The preacher said several times, "Once to live, once to die, and after this the judgment." Those are weighty words and not to be cast aside lightly.

Barbara told me that Weaverland used to be called Weber's Thal, or Weberthal. Martindale was Zimmerman's Crossing. My thoughts traveled back over the years to those olden days when people either walked to church or went on horseback, for carriages were considered too worldly in those days. I think I'll use the long-ago names of places here in my journal, just for the fun of it. They traveled Horseshoe Trail (Route 23) from *Saeune Schwamm Shtettle* (New Holland), *Katze Boucle Path*, the Paxton Trail (Route 322), and the Great Minquas Path (Route 340). Lancaster was Hickory Town and Harrisburg was Harris Ferry.

According to Grandpap, there was one, a Christian Zimmerman who lived several miles northeast of Weberthal, who weighed over 400 pounds. He was too heavy to ride a horse, so he built a cart to ride in and because of that he was not able to partake of Communion until the church had agreed to allow this new invention.

I once heard that in the long-ago days people even thought that raising geese was sinful, because they felt that the comfort of a feather bed is a peril to the soul.

Anyway, this 400-pound Christian was said to be the strongest man in the community. His great weight was not so much fat as it was muscle, bone and brawn. If reports are true, one day a man from Brandywine Town walked all the way to Christian's place to meet him. He himself was a very strong man, one who wanted to wrestle with Christian to try his strength against him. He said he hadn't met anyone yet he couldn't handle, and someone had dared him to tackle this 400-pound heavyweight.

Christian, being a Mennonite, was not interested in fighting or wrestling and told the man so. But the man wouldn't take no for an answer. He said he didn't walk all the way from Brandywine for nothing, and took off his coat and rolled up his sleeves. Christian, seeing there was no other way, told the man all right, but first they would have a drink of cider. He took the man out behind the barn where the full 35-gallon cider barrel stood. Christian opened the cap easily, lifted the entire barrel, tilted it, and took a swig, then set it down and motioned the man to do the same. Seeing those large well-muscled arms lift the barrel with such ease, the Brandy-wine man left without another word. Christian had figured that might get him ready to leave, and he was right.

Wow! That strong man story made Steven and Jonathan talk! They now are continually chinning themselves on a branch of the maple tree in the backyard, arm-wrestling, trying to bend nails, trying to lift a chair by its leg with one hand—doing all they can to strengthen their arm muscles. They also lift weights. I guess that's boys for you.

Ya well, it's suppertime, and then it's soon time for Barbara's young man to come. I sure don't want to miss that. I hope to at least get a glimpse of him as he walks toward the *nava stube* door. He comes every two weeks and Maria's fellow comes on the alternative Sunday evening, also every two weeks. How clever.

SUNDAY EVENING

What a lovely evening! The earth is green everywhere—green meadows, green leaves coming out on the trees and green fern fronds unfurling along the porch. The robins are singing joyously tonight, pouring out their joy to the lovely weather. Meadowlarks and red-winged blackbirds are trilling and dipping down to their nests, and the spring by the meadow fence is gurgling.

Patsy is chasing a bunny tail again and Tabby cat is curled up on the porch. Mumsy is writing a letter at the kitchen table and Grandpap is reading. Susanna and Naomi are getting ready to go to a Sunday evening gathering and Steven and Jonathan are playing checkers. Barbara is in the *nava stube* entertaining her beau George, and wouldn't I like to be a little mouse just now, observing them without being seen. When he drove in, I hid behind the big rosebush beside the washhouse door and peeked out as he walked up the path to the front *stube* door. I wasn't disappointed. He is quite handsome. Next Sunday evening I hope to get a glimpse of Maria's Dan.

After supper Maria and I went for a long walk, far beyond the mill and dam, past the *schwamm* where hundreds of frogs were poignantly croaking, then into the woods where the Conestoga flows ever onward to the west. Shy wildflowers bloomed along the bank. We sat on a rock enjoying the beauties of nature. Maria has the sweetest personality. Someday I hope to be just like her, if possible. We had a heart-to-heart chat and now I'm aiming for the lofty ideals and aspirations she has.

It's time to quit musing and daydreaming and head for bed.

ORDINATIONS

Mumsy was teaching me the art of cheese making today. Although I felt like the greenhorn I was, it was fun. After the supper dishes were washed, she told me to go get some fresh air and sunshine before the day is ended. She told me to get a pan of watercress from the spring beyond the mill. I'm the one that depletes the watercress supply the most—I sure love it on buttered bread—so I went, happily humming a glad tune.

A pair of cardinals whistled from a pine tree, mourning doves cooed from the roof of the mill, a cute little baby bunny scampered out from under a bush and I hope Patsy doesn't find it. They are so plentiful around here—cute when they're little, but destined to end up in Mumsy's frying pan eventually.

It was all so beautiful out there in the meadowlands. I was thinking back to my lonely and sad autumn and winter, and I could have wept for joy. I still miss Dad a lot, but the grief is almost all evaporated with the joys of a wonderful family all around me.

There's talk of another ordination on the horizon. At the supper table Grandpap was telling stories of how it went at different ordinations. At one ordination, the one in whose book the slip was found, thought it must have been a mistake—he got up and ran out the door, refusing to be ordained. Later he did give himself up to it, though.

In another ordination, the oldest candidate bypassed the first book, and so did all the others on down to the youngest who then picked up that book. In it was found the slip of paper that cast the lot on him. Later the oldest candidate was asked why he did not take the first book on the table. His reply was, "I wanted to take it, and I tried to take it, but my hand just had to take the next one." He felt that it was God-ordained to be so.

In another case, the night before a bishop ordination, one of the ministers dreamed that he saw the table and row of books in front of him, and a voice said, "Don't take the first book." He woke up and was thinking, "*Ach*, that was just a dream." He fell asleep again and dreamed the same dream again. He awoke and again decided, "it was just a dream." He fell asleep again and dreamed the same thing the third time. Then he went down on his knees beside the bed, and said, "Lord, if you don't want me to take that first book, I won't."

At the ordination the next day, being the oldest, he was the first one to choose a book. He bypassed the first book and took the second one. All the other ministers bypassed that one, too, until the last one had to take what was left. The slip was found in that book and so the lot fell to the youngest—God's chosen one. Grandpap said that dreams are usually meaningless, but because he dreamed it three times in a row so clearly, and woke up promptly afterward, he knew it was a message from God.

In 1894 there was an ordination at Weaverland Church and someone later wrote an article about it and sent it to the *New Holland Clarion*, or the *Ephrata Review*, I'm not sure which. Grandpap saved the article, and I found it between the pages of the big family Bible. I'll copy it here in my journal, for I've never attended an ordination. I think it would be a very somber, solemn occasion.

Choosing a Minister

Lancaster, Penna., March 23. The selection of a minister by the Mennonites, who worship at Weaverland, East Earl Township, this county, a few days ago, was an occasion that excited much interest in the neighborhood, and as early as daybreak the roads leading to the church at Weaverland were filled with carriages moving slowly through the deep mud. By 8 o'clock 300 vehicles were standing about the plain edifice and 1,200 men and women were packed inside.

There were 20 candidates for the ministry, all of whom were assembled in the church. The preliminary religious services in German and English, were conducted by the Rev. Christian Bombeyer, Bishop Eaby, and Bishop Shenk, and a dozen other reverend gentlemen made appropriate remarks.

At the conclusion of Bishop Shenk's sermon, the Rev. Messrs. Landis, Hartzler, and Buckwalter took 20 books, with clasps exactly alike to an ante-room, where they put in one of the books a slip of paper containing the words *"Ein Diener des Worts."*

The books were then taken into the main room and placed in a row on the table.

Each one of the candidates selected a book and retired to his seat. Bishop Martin arose and a solemn hush fell upon the great congregation. He approached the candidates and opened the books one after the other, until he reached the eleventh man in line, from whose book, when opened, fell the slip that bore the words giving him the title of a minister of the Gospel. The man who held the book was Menno S. Zimmerman, of Earl Township, was born on December 21, 1854, and ordained a minister at Weaverland March 8, 1884, at age 29 years.

The ceremony of opening the books lasted 15 minutes, and during that time the scene was impressive, men and women weeping aloud all over the church. The candidates showed evidence of intense excitement, all but Zimmerman, who was apparently cool and less concerned than any in the great crowd in the church.

Apple Blossom Time

I had a bit of a cough last evening and yet this morning, but I was still allowed to go along to Weberthal Church. (I like the old-fashioned names.) I like attending such a big church better than our small one back home. I sat very quietly and still and tried not to cough, so as not to disturb the other worshipers. The text was Romans 12, and the minister expounded on it very clearly and plainly. It is our own fault if we don't live according to what we have been taught.

After our Sunday dinner was over and the dishes were washed, I wandered down to the orchard, a delightful place just now—it's apple blossom time—a place of white-blossoming glory and the sweetest of bird songs. We had two days of rain last week that refreshed and renewed everything so, and probably made the fragrance of the blossoms all the sweeter.

A frisky squirrel chattered cheekily at my intrusion into its domain. I saw a woodchuck disappear underneath the stone wall and wondered if it had babies there. Seeing a log underneath a low-hanging apple bough, I made myself comfortable on it. As I gazed upward into my beautiful canopy, I was filled with wondrous awe that moved me to tears. The sunlight-dappled blossoms seemed to close in all around me, and I felt as if I was in a sanctuary or a reverent place like a church. Sitting there, dreamily drinking in the surrounding beauties of nature, I felt as if I was in a land of enchantment, a cocoon of peace and beauty which nothing could shatter. (I'm groping for the right words and not able to find them.)

Small creatures—mice and chipmunks—were scurrying over and around an old stump. They didn't seem to mind my presence at all. Birds were in the branches above me, and bees came to the blossoms. Butterflies came and went—God made so many beautiful things in this world.

Grandpap was telling stories again last night after the work was done—all the shoes were cleaned and polished for Sunday and the glass lamp globes sparkling clean. He told about a young girl, I think around a hundred years ago, who had ridden horseback to Weberthal Church, as the girls did in those days, sidesaddle, of course. A group of young people had made application to join the church that Sunday forenoon. The preachers that morning were very solemn, warning against false teachings and religions (probably Conrad Beissel's teachings from the Cloister), and of the reality of "Once to live and once to die, and after this the judgment."

After church, one of the girls who had expressed her desire to be baptized and to join the instruction class, led her horse to the big mounting stone and climbed on his back. The horse was skittish and high-strung, and hard to handle. Suddenly he reared, higher and higher, until he fell over backwards and the girl was underneath. The saddle horn punctured her abdomen and she lay white and still. Imagine the anguish of the bystanders, especially her family. She was still unconscious as the men carried her to the farm just east of the church where she died soon afterward. How they must have grieved over the loss of their loved one who was snatched away in the bloom of youth and health. But God's ways are not our ways, and if she had given her heart to the Lord, she was in a better place.

I did get to see Maria's Dan tonight and not just from peeking out from behind a rosebush. She invited me, Susanna and Naomi into the *nava stube* to meet him, and we stayed to visit awhile until she got "scouters," and then we left. Awhile later Marie came into the kitchen to get cookies and tea—the scouters wouldn't leave until she treated them. That's the custom around here, I suppose. Dan's a nice chap and he's sure lucky to get Maria.

Lilac Blossom Time

I'm sitting by the mill bridge again, reveling in the sweet fragrance of a bush laden with fragrant lavender lilacs, and in all the other beauties of an incomparable May evening. There's a robin's nest in the lilac bush and the four babies have already hatched.

Last evening we were taking pullets out to the range houses in the field after dark, with two big work horses hitched to the flat wagon. That sure was fun! The girls were singing—a song I barely knew. The words went something like this:

> Virtue is worth more than beauty or wit;
> In dark days, through old age, it comfortably fits.
> Oh, seek to develop its form and its love
> Until you are safely abiding above.

There were more stanzas but I couldn't memorize them all.

This afternoon Barbara sent me to her room to get her a clean apron, and I couldn't resist staying awhile to admire it. She has a beautiful quilt, both appliquéd and embroidered, in lavender and white, on her bed, and embroidered pillowcases and bureau

scarves. On her bureau I found a copy of "Ten Commandments for Married Couples," and "A Faithful Husband." So, it is just as I thought. She is getting married this fall. I asked Mumsy about it, and she just smiled mysteriously. Barbara is a good sport—she allowed me to bring her copies with me to put in my journal. She smiled knowingly, and said, "Someday you will have need of them." I don't know about that, but I still want them in my journal, so I'll start copying.

Ten Commandments for Married Couples

1. Thou shalt make Christ the Head of thy home. (Keep thy home on the rock of Jesus Christ and it shall stand in times of storm.)

2. Thou shalt readily forgive and overlook thy mate's faults and mistakes. (Be ye kind, tenderhearted, forgiving one another, loving one another.)

3. Thou shalt obey the Golden Rule. (Do unto others as you would have others do unto you.)

4. Thou shalt not let the sun go down upon thy wrath. (Apologize, ask forgiveness, pray together.)

5. Thou shalt compliment thy mate each day. (Focusing your attention on your mate's better qualities will generate more of the qualities you compliment.)

6. Thou shalt never criticize nor belittle thy mate. (Do away with impatience, worry, nagging, and jealousy.)

7. Thou shalt be more concerned with giving than getting. (Withhold nothing except by mutual consent, and for God's glory. Read I Corinthians 7.)

8. Thou shalt take time for love and companionship. (Build up your love by words and acts of appreciation for each other.)

9. Thou shalt take the time for wholesome recreation and worthwhile experiences. (Keep a sense of humor and learn to laugh at yourselves.)

10. Thou shalt give Christ first place in thy home. (Take time for daily Bible reading and prayer.)

A Faithful Husband

- Who can find a faithful husband? For his price is far above that of a "dream horse" or even a prosperous farm.
- The heart of his wife doth safely trust in him, whether he is at a horse sale, or comes home late from a farm sale.
- He tries to do the best for her and his family as long as he lives.
- He learns to use the tools of his trade and isn't afraid of a hard day's work.
- He is knowledgeable about church affairs and uses this for the family's enrichment.
- He rises early in the morning for his devotions and asks for wisdom for his daily tasks.
- He considers investments carefully and buys a home, or property, or business with an eye toward the future.
- He watches his health and gets the sort of exercise he needs to stay physically fit.
- His work is a good quality, even if he has to put in extra hours to make it that way.
- He doesn't neglect his home, and he attends barn raisings and frolics.
- He is concerned about his neighbors and tries to help those who are in need.
- He isn't afraid of difficult times because he has learned to trust God and has done what he could to provide for the family.
- He nourishes himself and his family both physically and spiritually.
- He wife is well thought of in their community because he never belittles her.
- He has a hobby that is relaxing and worthwhile.
- He is strong and honorable and is a happy person, easy to live with.

- His conversation is wide and uplifting—in fact, he makes it a rule of his life to speak kindly.
- He is interested in all things that concern his family and is not lazy or indifferent.
- His children love him and admire him, and his wife is proud of him and says, "Many have succeeded in this world, but you are the best of them all."
- Flattery is deceitful but a man who loves and fears God shall be truly praised, for his life proves that what he believes is real.

THUNDERSTORM

We had a heavy thunderstorm last evening, just as we were ready to go to the barn to do the chores. It kept on flashing and thundering, one hard crash after another and pouring down rain like a bucket emptying. We all walked down to the big Conestoga River (yes, it was a real river just then) to see the muddy, frothing water and bobbing tree branches and debris. It was really awesome, seeing the mighty power of the swirling waters. Even a half-submerged range house came bobbing along on the water. Caleb said he hopes it gets grounded somewhere before it hits a low bridge. It might have if it was swirled out to the side where the water was shallow. Luckily we're not that close to the Conestoga that our range houses had to be towed to higher ground.

Jonathan happened to pound his thumb with a hammer a few days ago. It throbbed and pained him so under the nail until he finally drilled a small hole in the nail, and then the pressure was released. They made him soak his thumb in Epsom Salt water for a good half hour. In Mumsy's copybook I found some more home remedies. Some I think are okay and others are amusing.

1. Soak red flannel in hot tallow and bind it around the neck for sore throat.

2. Tie bacon fat on cuts and sores to draw out infection.

3. Eat boiled onions and sugar to cure a cold.

4. Tie a rag soaked in a mixture of soap and vinegar on a painful boil to cure it.

5. Dog fat is a remedy for rheumatism.

6. A wool string tied around a finger will stop nosebleed.

7. Onion poultices tied to the soles of the feet should cure a fever.

In the old days, getting a doctor wasn't as easy as it is now. And then, they did crazy things like blood-letting and *braughing* (means powwowing). It's no wonder the people used home remedies. I'm so glad my cough is gone.

MORE OF GRANDPAP'S STORIES

We're sitting on the porch, and Mumsy is flicking *hossa* on the green painted rocker. Patsy is at my knee looking longingly up at Tabby, who has climbed upon the trellis. She's like a fiery spitball when he gets close, not afraid to use the claws that he respects.

The lilacs are still nice. I pinned a sprig on my apron bib, so I can enjoy the fragrance as I write.

Grandpap told the story of how the pulpit was torn out at Lichty's Church in 1889. When the new meetinghouse was nearly finished, the building committee, without the counsel of the church or ministers, decided to put a pulpit at the end of the singer's table instead of the usual preacher's table like in the other meetinghouses. When word of this spread through the community, a lot of people were very displeased. Someone felt they would be doing the bishop and the church a favor by removing it, without anybody finding out about it. On Thursday night, September 26, 1889, a man, his wife, two sons and daughter sneaked into the church in the dark of night and tore out the pulpit, fixed other boards in and replaced it with a preachers' table.

Well, instead of having done a favor, it worked just the opposite. It created a bitter storm of hard feelings and accusations, charges and counter charges. The finger of guilt was pointed toward Martin M. Zimmerman, because he had a key to the church. But he stoutly denied it, and verily he was innocently accused. A committee was appointed to go around to all the members of the church to question them. When they came to the guilty ones, the Mrs. asked loudly in German, "Do you think we would have done something like that?" Thus the committee was convinced they were innocent.

Two other innocent ones that were accused were Preacher Menno Zimmerman, whose ordination record I put in my journal, and Weaver Burkholder. One of their relatives had not been well, and they had gone to help take care of him. After the relative had died, another man saw the two in the orchard in earnest conversation. He stopped behind a tree and eavesdropped. He heard them say, "If only we had not taken him out, it might have been all right." He thought they said, "If only we had not taken *it* out," and jumped to the conclusion that they were the ones who had taken the pulpit out. (They were talking about the relative who had died a few hours after they had taken him to sit out on the porch for a while.) Through this misunderstanding a wild rumor spread like wildfire. When this false rumor had been put out, the finger of guilt still pointed to the innocent Martin M. Zimmerman. Almost everyone blamed him. He was excommunicated and every time he tried to come back and rejoin the church, the bishop told him, "Not until you confess to what you did."

The guilty ones were suffering from a troubled conscience. The mother would walk the floor, wringing her hands and saying, "This can't be right to let an innocent man carry the blame." They turned the mirrors toward the wall and sold some of their possessions, but still had no peace. Two of the daughters left the Mennonites and joined the Russelites (Jehovah's Witnesses). Their mother lamented that nothing was going right, seeming to be feeling the judgment of God. But it was not until 19 years after the pulpit was taken out, that she finally went to the bishop and confessed the sin of her family.

The bishop, deep in grief, rushed to the home of Martin M. Zimmerman and went down on his knees in front of him beseeching forgiveness for having refused him membership all those years. Martin was greatly relieved to be cleared and to be received once again into the church. Nineteen years was a long time to have innocently been considered guilty.

Grandpap said that human nature is still much the same as it was then. Satan is still busy trying to deceive people and lead them astray. He said, "Watch and pray, lest ye enter into temptation and be deceived thereby." Mumsy says that the important thing is to keep on and never give up, getting up every time we fall, confessing our sins and pressing forward toward the mark of the prize.

PIE MAKING DAY

A warm day to be baking, so we were very glad for the outdoor bake oven. I was churning butter (it seemed to take an extra long time) while Mumsy made the pie crusts, and the girls cooked the filling—raisin, mincemeat, and butterscotch.

Maria told of a time when she was very young and worked for Uncle Titus. She was not a very experienced pie-maker yet, and the crusts turned out hard. At the supper table, Uncle Titus tapped the crust with his knife, whistled softly under his breath, and said, "*Socaments.*" It was a most embarrassing moment, she said.

Well, she has since become a pie-making expert, after all the practice she has had. One of the girls wrote a poem about Grandma's pies which I'll copy here.

Grandma's Pies

When I sit back and close my eyes,
I still remember Grandma's pies,
All in a row on baking day,
Her handiwork there on display.

I still recall the spicy smell,
Her kitchen that I loved so well.
I wish I could go back once more
And see her standing at the door.

Then she would cut a slice for me,
And join me with her cup of tea.
Oh, how I long for days gone by,
For one more slice of Grandma's pie.

But cherished memories remain,
When I walk down memory's lane,
Of Grandma's pies and Grandma's love,
A blessing sent from God above.

I don't remember much at all of Mumsy's mother, only what I hear the girls tell about her. She was a jewel of a wife and raised a large family. In her tongue was the law of kindness and wisdom; strength and honor were her clothing; her children called her blessed, and the heart of her husband could safely trust in her. She did him good and not evil all the days of her life, like it says in Proverbs 31.

RUNAWAY HORSE

We're having sweet, balmy, beautiful weather. Barbara and I weeded the strawberry patch this morning. The turtledoves were gently cooing from the big pine. I thought they're supposed to sing before a rain, but this was just after a rain. I guess they coo whenever they please.

The weeds pulled easily after the rain, and Barbara kept our task from getting monotonous—she told me interesting things as we worked. One was of the wild ride she and George had coming home from a wedding last winter.

Just as the hostlers brought their horse Rex, hitched to the buggy and up to the front walk, the *gleppering* (serenading) began. Rex heard all that noise, and was he ever excited then! It took three hostlers to hold on to him while she and George hopped in. Rex tore out of their hands and was off like a shot, and out the lane. As he turned onto the road, the buggy was on two wheels, but then righted again and careened on its way. Out the winding Creek Road they fairly flew, or so it seemed, she said.

They thought they'd land in the creek for sure. But the horse knew the way and on they cruised—up hill, down hill, around the corners they went. They both hung on to the lines trying to hold him back, as hard as they could, but it made no difference to Rex. He wanted to go, and go they did, at top speed. Barbara said she doesn't know who was shaking the most, she, George or the horse. She said they went right through the crossings and stop signs, but luckily there was hardly any traffic at that time of night. Coming down Zimmerman's Road, while they were pulling on the lines with all their might, the right line suddenly tore. Oh no! That left them with no control of the horse anymore. Barbara said that would have been one thrilling ride if they would have known they'd get home safely, but it looked mighty doubtful to them.

Rex was galloping wildly, careening over the road from side to side. Then, to complicate matters still more, a Model T Ford came from behind. He must not have noticed that the horse was not under their control, for he tried to pass just then. George, seeing the danger, sprang out of the buggy and onto the shaft at the horse's side. Holding on to the harness he inched forward toward the torn line. The trees were whizzing past, and the rocks beside the road looked dangerously close as the horse dug in still more. Finally George was able to grasp the torn line and guided the horse into the field on the right, and then with Barbara's help with the other line, they were able to stop him. The Ford stopped, too. The man got out, as angry as could be, and gave them a bad tongue-lashing. George said, rather shakily, "I'm sorry sir, I couldn't help it, my line tore." Finally, after having vented his anger, the man drove off. George and Barbara shakily unhitched the horse. They were almost at Barbara's home then, and George led Rex home and later came back for the buggy.

Barbara said that was the most hair-raising ride of her life. They were so thankful for God's protecting hand that got them home safely. She already didn't have a very high opinion of noisily serenading a newlywed couple and now she's more opposed to it than ever. It caused *Dumheita*, that time anyway.

Time to go help Mumsy in the garden.

Hans Graf

Here's another one of Grandpap's after-supper stories.

In the early days when the settlers were coming cross the ocean to Penn's Woods, Hans Graf (later spelled Groff) owned land in Germantown first, then went farther west. One day his oldest son and their hired man were out looking for their runaway horses. They found them grazing near a place where there were large, beautiful oak trees and huge black walnut trees in a lush meadow where three bubbling springs of pure, fresh water bubbled out of the ground and made a stream of water. They figured that the soil there must be the most fertile in the area, for where the wood grows heaviest, the soil must be the best. They figured those springs would never dry up, so they built their homestead there and put on it a well-built stone house and substantial barns.

Now comes the story of how he came to have two wives. It wasn't intentional. Everyone felt sorry for him and just as sorry for both of his wives. When Hans still lived in Switzerland, his father was a rich and well-known governmental official. Hans followed in his father's footsteps. After he had gotten the training to be a general in the army, he married a girl who was also of high rank. They had one son. Then, much to his wife's dismay, Hans became influenced by Anabaptist teachings. He was re-baptized, choosing to suffer persecution with the people of God, turning his back on his riches and position. His wife did not share his beliefs. She refused to leave the state church, so Hans left Switzerland without her.

He still loved his wife and returned to Switzerland a number of times to beg her to join him in America. This was done in utmost secrecy, because the law forbade her to help him in any way, or she would be cast into prison. When their son was 5 years old, Hans had him brought to America. Soon after that, some immigrants told Hans that his wife had died.

Hans later married a second time to a young woman named Anna Herr. They bought 300 acres near Strasburg and moved there. They had been married for over 20 years and had nine children when Hans' brother Martin Graf came to America. He informed his brother that his first wife was still living—it was someone else by the same name who had died. What a shock that must have been!

Hans could not rightfully live with his second wife anymore after that. Soon after, his first wife became an Anabaptist and came to America to find her husband and son. It was unbelievable to her to find that her husband had another family in America, but she took the blame upon herself. Hans built a cabin for her and a small one for himself, choosing to live in solitude the rest of his life. He provided for his two wives and their families. All three of them lived peaceably, in righteousness, making the best of the situation. Someone said of Hans, "He is a respectful, faithful witness wherever he goes."

Nowadays people divorce and remarry as they please, thinking there is nothing wrong with it. And yet, God's laws never change, be it in the 18th century or the 20th.

A Trip to Hickory Town

We (the girls and I) went to Lancaster yesterday on the trolley, and my thoughts traveled back over the years to when people were heading west in covered wagons through Hickory Town and Harris Ferry and on out to the Buffalo Valley. Now there are so many tall buildings and traffic, tooting horns and people walking on the sidewalks.

Barbara let me in on her secret. She had gone to get her wedding dress goods! She and George are to be married on the second Thursday of November. After the shopping was done and she had selected her soft gray fabric, she bought us each a bowl of oyster stew—the first time I ever tasted it. I didn't think it was as good as I expected it to be, the way they bragged it up, but I didn't let on since she was kind enough to buy it for me. They bought me an autograph book, too, and Barbara wrote this verse in it:

> The roses are red, the leaves are green;
> The days are past that we have seen.
> May we all meet in that sweet land
> Where we shall take no parting hand.

This afternoon Susanna hitched Blackie to the cart and she and I went for a drive out to Goodville, to get a recipe from one of her friends living on a nearby farm. A cool breeze was blowing from the west, and purple martins swooped and warbled from the pole lines.

The field corn is up, the gardens are lush and beautiful, and the flowerbeds are so nice. I can understand why this is called the "Garden Spot of America."

Susanna asked me if I was ready to be rid of my braids and put my hair up into a bob? "Yes," I told her, "I think it is time." And so, when we got home she found me a hairnet and helped me with it. I practiced over and over until they said it was good enough. Maria is making a *kapp*, or covering, for me, and I am to get a new bonnet, too.

Mumsy said that I am now leaving childhood behind and should remember the following verse: "Whose adorning let it not be that outward adorning of plaiting the hair, and of wearing of gold, or of putting on of apparel, but let it be the hidden man of the heart, in that which is not corruptible, even the ornament of a meek and quiet spirit, which is in the sight of God of great price." (1 Peter 3: 3,4)

I came down to the mill bridge tonight and sat thinking over the weeks I've been here. I thought of the Bible verse: "Sorrow and weeping may endure for a night; but joy cometh in the morning." There are a lot of sorrows and heartaches in this sinful world, but someday God's children will be with the Saviour, and all tears will be wiped away from their eyes. No more tears and no more crying.

The Cloister

Grandpap was telling of maybe 200 years ago when Conrad Beissel (later called Father Friedsam) was in this area and luring people to his Settlement of the Solitary at Ephrata. Beissel proclaimed that Saturday should be kept as the Sabbath Day, and divine services should be held then. He taught that it is wrong to eat meat, that a spiritual person should not marry, and even encouraged some wives to leave their husbands and husbands to leave their wives. If reports are correct, one man was so afraid that his wife would desert him and move out to the Cloister, that he tied her to the bedpost.

Even some Mennonites were fascinated by Beissel's teachings and followed after him. They thought that in the Settlement they would be safe from the vanities of the world, and that it would be the way to true holiness. Beissel claimed to have special visions and revelations from God, and that even before he came to America he was ordained by God to bring his vision here.

On the lintel above the door at the entrance to the Cloister they had this verse:

The house is entered through this door
By peaceful souls who dwell within;
Those who have come will part no more,
For God protects them here from sin.

In Beissel's congregation was a young girl not yet baptized, who fell ill and sent for Conrad Beissel to baptize her before she died. Arriving at night, Beissel insisted that the baptizing must be done in a flowing stream. The parents were opposed to this because of the wintry weather and the girl's illness. Beissel finally yielded and put the girl in a tub of cold water. Beissel would usually dunk his converts three times backwards into the water to undo any previous baptisms of other faiths and the old sinful life, and then three times forward to start the Christian life anew. But because this girl was sick he just poured water over her head three times. Even so, the girl died soon afterwards.

Reports have it also that one cold, snowy night there was a big, bright star with a tail in the sky—a glowing comet. Beissel sent out riders with a message for the people. They stopped at every cabin, calling out, "Arise to meet the Lord! The end of the world is at hand!" The people sprang out of bed, and when they saw the great comet in the east with its fiery tail, setting the heavens aglow, many were exceedingly afraid.

The riders made frantic gestures toward the sky, and called out, "See God's sign in the heavens! The brothers from the Cloister sent me to warn the people." Then they would turn and gallop onto the next place. Many settlers fled to the Cloister for refuge, some on horseback, some running, with lanterns swaying in the darkness, and some with candles sputtering in the wind.

The brothers and sisters in the Cloister fasted and prayed, and felt blessed to be under Father Friedsam's spiritual leadership. They lead very austere lives. Some fasted so much they became malnourished. They pounded acorns to make meal for bread, and some even ate only that. They slept on hard, narrow wooden benches with a block of wood for a pillow. The doorways were low, to teach people humility by stooping low when they go through them. They were also narrow, some only 16 inches wide, and only the slender could get through.

They each got a new, holy name, to help them forget the sins and the vanities of the world. They knelt for hours at a time on the cold, hard floor, praying. They also fashioned religious texts in intricate designs, and they had a bakery where they baked bread to give to the poor. They made their own paper and had a printing shop where they bound their own books with leather tanned in the Settlement.

In 1783 when the war was nearly over, several British prisoners escaped from Hickory Town and headed toward the seacoast. The escapees stopped at Mennonite farms to ask for a place to sleep, and for food. As good Mennonites will generally do, three families gave the prisoners food and lodging, not meaning to be traitors at all. But local military officials found it out, and called it treason. They insisted on punishing the three families and so they were arrested.

Peter Miller of the Cloister was a friend of George Washington, and interceded for them saying that they were merely obeying the Biblical command: "If thine enemy hunger, feed him." The arrested ones were then pardoned and set free.

And so we can see that even though Beissel's beliefs were off center, he and his people did much good. They sang beautifully and harmoniously. They counted it a joy to deny self and serve the Lord, which we all should do, and live in contentment with our lot in life.

A Walk in the Woods

Early this morning Naomi and I went for a walk in the woods, or the *buschland*, as Grandpap calls it. The birds were just awakening and starting their full-throated chorusing, and baby bunnies were hopping about looking for clover. We stopped to listen to a strange bird. Then, not far from us, the green fern fronds on the banks of the run parted and a wild turkey gobbler came to the water to drink, followed by a hen and her poults.

Just then a movement on the ridge above us caught my eye, and there stood a graceful buck, its eyes alert to any surrounding dangers. I grabbed Naomi's arm. The movement sent him bounding away, and scattered the turkeys with frightened gobbles.

Peace and contentment surrounded us. We took deep breaths of the fragrance of the woodland scents—the leaves on the trees and the creek water, as the birds serenaded us. We cut watercress out of the spring, then headed for home, satisfied and refreshed by our morning walk.

Naomi said there used to be an Indian settlement just north of Weberthal. They were all on good terms with the settlers because of the fair treaty William Penn made with them. They would even gather in some of the settlers' cabins to share the warmth of the hearth and to trade game and fish for bread. One of the immigrants, by consulting his almanac, was able to predict an eclipse of the moon—even the very night it would appear. On that evening, 50 Indians gathered at his cabin to witness a miracle. It happened just as he predicted to the great astonishment and amazement of the Indians. After a time of awed silence, one of them said, "It is the white man's God who tells him this, else he would not know it."

The Indian children and the settlers' children played together. The Indian boys were nearly naked, so the white youths would also discard some of their clothes so they would be more equal. Then they'd have foot races and tusseling matches and contests with their bows and arrows. Almost always the Indian boys won, which amused the chiefs who were watching.

Ya well, Susanna is calling me and I must go. I can hardly wait until the strawberries are ready.

A Family Gathering

Mumsy had invited all the family, including the married ones and all their youngsters to come for dinner on Sunday after Weberthal Church services. I'm getting to know my cousins better, but it *shpeids* me there's not a girl cousin near my age. The two oldest cousins are boys—the oldest girl is only 9 years old. Mumsy roasted a turkey and made giblet gravy and filling, mashed potatoes, dried corn, and pickles. For dessert there were three kinds of pies, puddings and mixed fruit. My, this is a big family—it seems like I'll never get to know my aunts well enough to know which name goes with which face. Aunt Lovina, the youngest married one, I know. She and Abe live just over the field from here and come over often with little Amos.

It seemed like everyone was talking, laughing, and visiting at once, with the toddlers laughing and running, and babies crying and cooing and everyone taking turns to play with them and hold them. The men took chairs and sat out under the shade tree to visit. The school-age children went down to the run to splash and wade. Mumsy served cold meadow tea and pretzels when they came back.

No one was hungry for supper tonight, so we didn't bother making any. In the evening Susanna, Naomi and I, along with Steven and Jonathan, went boating on the Conestoga. It was a surprisingly cool evening. Mumsy made me wear a sweater. There was a silvery moon hanging over the treetops and the stars were twinkling. The moon's silvery light cast mysterious shadows over the trees along the creek. A screech owl's quavering cry came from a treetop, and an answering call came from another up the creek.

The girls were talking about *rumshpringing*, singings, beaus and such stuff. Susanna told us another secret—Caleb is getting married, too, this fall, probably in November. I can hardly wait.

STRAWBERRY TIME

Strawberries, strawberries everywhere. That's something Dad and I never got enough of when we were alone, for we didn't have our own berry patch. Mumsy and the girls are canning, canning, canning, and I am picking, capping, and eating them to my heart's content.

Grandpap talked of the old days of the first settlers, when honey and molasses was probably their only sweetener. One old grandmother had such a sweet tooth that she sent one of her sons to Hickory Town with a bit of money to buy some for her. When he returned he was ringing a cowbell—he had found more necessary use for her money; for cowbells were a necessity to find straying cattle in the woods. The old lady was so disappointed that she sat down and wept, for she had been so eagerly looking forward to his return. Later, that man's cow, in spite of the bell, wandered into the swamp near Saeue Schwamm and drowned.

Another story was of a Mennonite man from Hammer Creek who married a Lutheran woman. While he was away on a trip, she took the children to be baptized in the Lutheran church. The man was so displeased that at the next gathering in the Lutheran church he rode his horse right in the church door and up and down the aisles. He was arrested and heavily fined for such behavior.

Another report is of a Mennonite girl name Fiana who eloped with a Dunkard boy. The young man was working at carpentering a house near Zimmerman's Crossing, and Fiana was working for her aunt and uncle at a neighboring farm. They became acquainted and fell in love. Her parents were very much opposed and forbade her to see him. One Sunday afternoon, instead of going to church, they galloped away together to be married. Her parents were deeply grieved and saddened. They had a farm all ready for their only child, hoping a Mennonite man would come along for her. Let's hope he was a nice decent man, and made her a good husband anyway,

Ya well, I must get back to my berries, and then mix up a steam pudding in time for supper. It goes well with crushed strawberries.

THE SWANS

One evening last week when I walked down to the bridge, there were two elegant looking swans on the millrace, serenely floating side by side. It was a beautiful sight and I ran back to tell the others to come see them. Soon afterward, two Amish boys came walking along the Conestoga, each carrying a long switch and herded the swans homeward. It *schpeided* me so to see them for they were beautiful! Then, the next evening, lo and behold, there were the swans again! Sure enough, soon the same two boys came for their swans and drove them homeward. I would have liked to talk with the boys but I was too shy. I wonder if they walked all the way from Churchtown?

For some reason those swans really must have loved the millrace, because the next day they were back again. The boys were soon there for them, and apparently they won, for the swans haven't come back since.

Naomi and Jonathan had a grand tiff on Saturday. It started with Jonathan bringing one of those green striped carrot caterpillars into the house. Naomi was on her hands and knees scrubbing the floor. Jonathan showed her the "cute" thing, then dropped it down the neck of her dress. She did just what I think he wanted her to do, scream and then chase him (after getting rid of the caterpillar). They were at it all day long. I'm not sure what all they did to each other, but by Sunday it was over and they had forgiven each other again, for they both went along on our walk to the *buschland* in the evening and everything was peaceful. We made a bonfire and sat around it, talking and bantering, while the golden moon rose up over the treetops and the enchantment of the night enveloped us. Susanna played softly on her harmonica—sweet, haunting, romantic strains. Then she and Naomi sang a duet— sweet, melodious and tender. I cherish these times of family togetherness so, remembering how it was when I was with Aunt Hepsi and was so lonely and sad.

Psalm 104 (In Rhyme)

Great is the Lord, My soul shall bless Thee,
Thou are clothed in honor and majesty;
Thy garments are light and the heavens are Thine;
Stretched as a curtain while moon and stars shine;
Beams of Thy chambers in waters are laid,
The clouds we see for Thy chariots are made,
On wings of the wind Thy presence I know,
Angels are ministers to us below,
The earth's foundations laid with Thy hand,
Till the end of time unmovable stands.

BREAD MAKING

Naomi is teaching me how to make bread. I've been trying to get the texture of the dough just right and then kneading it for all I'm worth, for she told me that is the secret to good, light bread. She says you can knead love into the dough, and that makes the job seem easier. Well, it's true, because I tried it. I dearly love this wonderful family, the rambling farmhouse, the big barn and all the fields, woods and meadowland, and so it was easy to put that love to work. I'll copy a little poem here I found, about love and baking.

Mama's Baking

Mama's the finest cook on earth.
She told me long ago,
Bread's no good unless you add
Some loving to the dough.
"And when you're baking pies," she said,
"A pinch of faith and trust,
If added to the shortening,
Makes a flaky, tender crust."
Compassion by the spoonful,
In the batter of a cake,
Makes it come out light and fluffy,
And the finest you can make.
Now these things cannot be purchased,
In the store across the way,
But Mama keeps them in her heart,
And uses them each day.

After the bread was baked, Naomi and I took a loaf to old Mrs. Ziemer who is 82 years old and lives in the Daudi end of our neighbor's house. She was so pleased, and asked us to stay and visit awhile. She served us grape juice, homemade cheese, and pretzels. We talked about the recent ordination that I never even got around to mentioning in my journal because I didn't attend it. The chosen one was someone I didn't know. They told me the church house would get too full if everyone went, and that we must leave room for the relatives of those in the class or lot. I was so curious about it, because in that article about Menno's ordination it said that men and women were weeping aloud all over the church. Aloud? I asked Mrs. Ziemer about it (she attended the ordination because her nephew was in the lot). "Yes," she said, "there was plenty of weeping, but no one wept aloud. Becoming so vocal was perhaps kind of a custom in the old days, but now they realize it's not necessary, and more Christian to weep quietly if they must weep."

Naomi asked her about the place where the Spring Grove Forge used to be—a large mansion with many rooms and slave headquarters. But that will have to wait until next time for Barbara is calling me to take peppermint water out to the menfolk working in the fields. It's a job I like, except for the stubble in the fields that hurt my feet. If I'd have a little brother, he would get the job.

THE MANSION

In the days of slavery, the mansion provided room at one end for all the slaves on the big farm. During the time the Forge was in operation, there was a row of shacks along the Conestoga Creek where the workers lived. The mansion stood on the edge of the slope that led down to the Conestoga. The whole hillside was wooded and filled with thick undergrowth, which extended far along the woods that bordered the Conestoga.

Tall horse-chestnut trees stood on the front lawn. Behind the house, in the woods, a large pack of hounds was kept in a shed. In a den under the tobacco shed foxes were kept that they had captured for their fox chases. They stayed in the dark corners of the den and appeared only at feeding time.

Those fox chases were fascinating to the neighborhood boys, even though they had been taught by their parents that it was a sinful, worldly sport. It was usually on a brisk cold Saturday in late November, when the fox chases were held. The place was a center of excitement in the community on that day. A huckster table was set up near the barn, where coffee, tea, candy, sandwiches, peanuts, pretzels and cookies were sold to the hungry riders and the spectators. They'd usually choose a day when light snow was on the ground, in order to track the foxes better. They would make a bonfire near the huckster table, and gather round it to warm themselves from the brisk, chilly wind while they drank their coffee. The neighbor boys liked to watch the horsemen arrive, one after another, arrayed in pride and splendor. The horses would be puffing out their frosty breath, pawing and prancing impatiently. Now and then one would rear upright in his eagerness to get into the chase. If one fell over backward, the riders would nimbly jump away from their horses and avoid getting hurt. I had to think of that girl at Weberthal Church whose horse fell over and she was underneath. God must have needed her in His garden of love.

When the foxes were brought out of the den and exposed to the hounds, a furor of howling and yelping arose and a frenzy of wild barking. Then off they went, tearing through the fields and thick undergrowth, after the foxes. The horses were trained to jump fences and ditches and logs. No one ever knew which way the fox would turn, so it was a frantic, wild dashing back and forth until at last a fox was cornered and captured. They were usually several miles way and it was several hours later until the last fox had been captured and the excitement was over. Back to the fire and the huckster table came the colorful riders, puffing and panting as they came to a standstill.

Mrs. Ziemer talked about other interesting things, too, which I want to put into my journal, but that will have to wait, for it's time to help in the garden now.

HOBOS

Now I'm back with a tumbler of delicious meadow tea, after hoeing four long rows of sweet corn. It's good to sit here on the porch rocker and rest.

Mrs. Ziemer also told about the tramps or hobos in the community, who came to the door for either a meal to eat right away, or something to put into their sacks for eating later. They were mostly elderly men who had wasted their money in their younger years, by gambling or by strong drink, and had come out to the rural areas by jumping freight trains. They befriended each other, and gathered in sheltered spots in the Conestoga Valley, such as under a cliff along a stream bank or in a hollow. They would use broken limbs off of trees to start a bonfire to make coffee, and to keep warm in winter. On cold, rainy days they found shelter in the church house sheds. Mrs. Ziemer said that the tramps knew they had better stay on the sunny side of the good-natured farmers' wives because they depended on their generosity for survival.

There was one named Irish Milk who earned his meals and barn lodging by splitting wood, mending fences, cleaning and greasing harnesses, and other jobs. He had his coffee den under the big trees along the creek, west of the mansion. One Sunday a group of boys wandered by his place, and seeing him sitting there decided to try to get a rise out of him. They teased and angered him by calling him names and threw sticks and stones into his place. Irish Milk was furious, and in his rage picked up his big club and ran after them. They had thought he was an old, slow bum, but found out he was surprisingly fast and gaining on them. He raised his club high above his head and they ran for dear life. Seeing that he was going to get them, they jumped into the creek and swam across. They felt they had a close call, and left him alone after that, for he told them in no uncertain terms what he would do if they tried something like that again.

There was an old couple, Mr. and Mrs. Thomas, who were road walkers and carried their own cooking utensils. At the farmhouses they would ask for vegetables, noodles and sometimes a little meat, and do their own cooking on their campfire. There was a Rosie Tompson who could be trusted not to steal. She was a heavily built, middle-aged Italian woman who carried two heavy satchels. She wouldn't have won a beauty contest, but she was very friendly as she laid out her wares on the table for the farm wife to see them. She had shoelaces, garters, paring knives, safety pins, baby bibs, sewing thread, needles and thimbles. If she was hungry, she would ask for some buttermilk and bread. She'd crumble the bread in her bowl, then slice green onions over it and pour the buttermilk over it all. She would sit down and eat it with the same relish that we would eat a bowl of ice cream or a slice of cold watermelon.

There were also chicken thieves that plagued the farmers. A good watch dog was a necessity. There was one outfit that held fake revival meetings. The thieves would scan the crowd, and then know which farms to visit that night—they'd know who wasn't at home.

There were also some crafty horse thieves around. There was one farmer who had a fiery black horse that was the envy of the neighborhood. For speed and stamina he couldn't be beat. One day the farmer drove him to New Holland and tied him in the shed. When he got back several hours later, the horse was gone. He contacted the police immediately, knowing he had tied the horse securely, and that he must have been stolen.

Several days later Maryland police found a black man in a cart driving a good quality horse and became suspicious. Via the telephone they discovered that a horse of such a description had been stolen in New Holland, and so they arrested the man and returned the horse. The farmer got his horse back, but he wasn't the same anymore. He had been driven too far and too fast which ruined him—his speed and stamina were gone.

Ya well, the birds are singing their goodnight vespers and it's getting damp and chilly out here under the apple tree. I must get inside. Grandpap is heading out to close the range shelters for the night so that no foxes or weasels get the pullets. The boys are coming in from horseback riding.

My cough and pain in the side are all better. For this I am ever so thankful. I hope it never comes back.

Psalm 139

Lord, Thou hast searched my heart, my every thought dost know,
Thou knowest all my ways; Wherever I may go.
For there is not a word; But Thou does hear me say;
From Thy loving presence I cannot flee away.
Neither shall the darkness conceal or cover me;
The darkness and the light are both alike to Thee.

PART TWO

Summertime

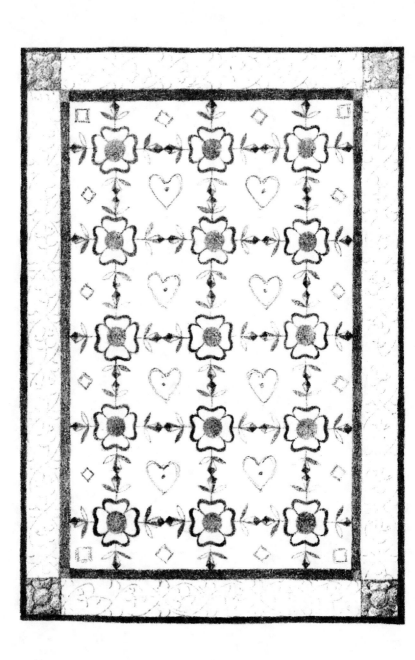

Berry Picking

Today Susanna, Naomi and I wandered the wooded banks of the Conestoga, hunting wild raspberries. The woods were astir with trilling birds, sun-dappled shadows, and the chirping of insects. We passed our favorite picnicking spot by the trickling spring and beds of mint. There's a circle of rock for a fire, and a large flat rock on a stump for a table. We sat there to rest awhile, dreaming of sometime having a large family picnic there with all the married brothers and sisters (my aunts and uncles) along, too. We could hitch the work horses to the flat wagon and drive back the field lane.

Little striped chipmunks darted here and there—so cute and pert. We got a glimpse of a doe and a fawn on the ridge; with a flick of their tails they disappeared. A pair of excited bluejays called attention to a red fox slinking away in the shadows along a trail into a thicket.

We girls wandered from thicket to thicket, chattering away while we filled our buckets. Susanna had a scare when she went farther into the thicket for handfuls of the plump, juicy purple berries. As she was turning around to come back out, there, right in front of her was a big, black, snake, curled up, with its head raised. She screamed and tried to back up, but the thorns pricked her. There was no way out except over the snake. Naomi offered to throw stones at it, but Susanna was afraid she'd drive it toward her. Finally it slithered away, much to Susanna's relief.

When our buckets were full we quenched our thirst at the trickling spring, then sat on a log, too full of berries to head right back. We rested awhile, again enjoying the lovely scenery. I like it

when the girls talk about *rumshpringing*. Naomi was teasing Susanna about a certain boy that she claims is keeping close tabs on her, but Susanna denies it vehemently, and says she'd rather be an old maid for a hundred years than take him. Naomi said, "That's a very good sign, for that which we throw farthest away is what we will someday fetch again." Then she scolded her for talking like that, for he's a quiet, good-natured and handsome boy. If Mumsy could have heard them she'd have put a stop to such talking right away, I'm sure. She says "Little pitchers have big ears," and I'm keeping them open.

As we were enjoying the beauties of the woodland—the fresh breezes and the delightful woodsy aromas—the comradship and the fellowship of the girls made it seem all the lovelier. Someday I'd like to build a little house back here, and live here among the beauties of nature. I'd want Maria to live with me, but I guess Dan would have something to say to that. Any one of the other girls would be fine, too, but I guess that will never happen. Oh well, it doesn't hurt to dream.

We came on home with visions of raspberry pies, jams, jellies and cobblers in our heads, knowing it was well worth getting our arms scratched up and jumping over snakes to get them.

Here's a little poem I like, suitable for our woodland ramblings:

Give me friendly little woods,
A gently bubbling spring,
A winding brook that ripples by,
While happy birdsongs ring.
A dear friend to walk with me,
Communing, hand-in-hand;
While eyes and ears and heart respond
To wonders God has planned.
A mossy log where we may rest,
An hour to meditate.
This is an ideal setting that
I classify first rate.

ONE GIRL'S VOYAGE

This morning Barbara introduced me to the art of milking a cow. It looked so easy, but when I squeezed, nothing came out until I learned to use my thumb to coax the milk downward and direct the stream of frothy milk into the bucket. I'm going to help milk the cows every morning from now on, and soon I should be an expert, too.

Maria told me tonight that when they were children, at bedtime, when the bedtime stories had been told and the lisping prayers heard, Mumsy would gather up the baby and belongings, and head for the stairs, calling, "All aboard!" All the children would follow and troop up the stairs after her. It made me smile to think of it, and sorry that I missed those days.

"All aboard!" This makes me think of our people several hundred years ago, boarding ships to come to this new land. ALL ABOARD, for better or for worse—there was no turning back.

I read of the story of a young girl named Marguerite, just 17 years old, coming to America with her mother, close to 200 years ago. Her mother got very sick on the ship, but there was no doctor to be had. All around them were miles and miles of restless waves, and above them were the billowing sails, with the ship rocking on the swells. Marguerite tearfully bathed her mother's feverish brow and did all she could to make her more comfortable. The drinking water on board became stale and covered with thick scum. The broiling summer sun scorched them. Hunger, thirst, and fatigue made them all short-tempered and irritable.

Many were dying, and the day came that Marguerite's mother was also wrapped in a canvas shroud and heaved over the side of the ship into the relentless waves. Marguerite was cast into the depth of grief and despair for the rest of the journey.

Finally the shore was reached, and the heart-broken girl disembarked.

In Germantown a kind lady—an angel in disguise—took Marguerite under her wings. She took her into her own home, fed her nourishing meals and put her into one of her featherbeds to sleep. When she was strong enough to travel, she went with Christian and Anna Herr to stay awhile in their home until her uncle could come for her.

They traveled in a big covered wagon drawn by two sturdy horses. They camped that night in a grassy meadow by a creek under the spreading branches of a sycamore tree, while the horses cropped fresh green grass. The birds twittered their goodnights as a hoot owl's quavering notes echoed from a tree. Next day they forded the Schuylkill River.

When they arrived at Christian and Anna Herr's homestead, Marguerite was impressed by the well-built stone house with the date "1719" carved into the lintel over the front door. There was a huge central fireplace in the *kuche* (kitchen), a built-in corner (*eck*) bench, and a *schnitzel* bunk.

Anna Herr soon had a savory stew bubbling in the pot on the raised hearth. Christian's father (Daudy Hans) lived there, too, with his son and family, and seemed almost like the head of the home. On Sunday settlers came from far and near to have church services there in the *stube*, and both Hans and Christian preached a sermon. They felt that the most precious thing in this new land was religious freedom. The Switzers (as the others in the new world called them) had suffered much for their faith. Many were burned at the stake, drowned, and killed with the sword. But they had a living hope and did not fear a martyr's death. Their inner peace and joy, while going to their deaths, was noticed by the bystanders who had come to watch the executions.

They witnessed the calm inner strength that came from a power beyond themselves, and wanted for themselves what the martyrs had and their numbers increased. It was the faith of our fathers, living still, in spite of dungeon, fire and sword.

I imagined the Herrs in their stone house near Strasburg working in the fields—the men swinging their axes all day long, clearing land for crops, plowing a straight furrow in the rich, dark earth, building barns and hunting game, and everything else it took to carve a homestead out of the wilderness.

I imagined Anna Herr in her stone house—cooking meals on the big raised hearth, making lye soap for the scrubbing laundry, churning butter and baking golden loaves of bread, swingling flax and carding wool, and dipping and molding candles, with nimble fingers. Their trust must have been in the Lord to see them through the dangers there in the new land, where bears and cougars still roamed the forests and hardships on every side.

Psalm 121

I lift my eyes unto the hills, Whence cometh help for me;
The Lord created Heaven and earth; He my help must be.
He will not let my foot be moved; For He shall never sleep;
And over all His people here; A watch shall ever keep.
Through light or darkness ever near, When I come or go;
Deliverance from every fear; I will surely know.

MEMORIES OF TERESA

Barbara was telling me about the little girl Grandpap and Mumsy used to babysit for, from the time she was a toddler until she went to school. She and Barbara were the best of friends— she still talks about what a nice little girl Teresa was. Teresa is all grown up now, but recently she sent by mail (at Barbara's request) a fat pack containing some of her memories of when she was with her babysitters on the farm. Barbara gave me permission to copy them in my journal. I was thrilled, for I love to hear of cherished memories of days gone by. Here are Teresa's memories:

DOWN ON THE FARM

From the earliest I can remember until I was in grade school, I spent time with my babysitters. I have very fond memories of those days. As I look back over those years my heart fills with joy. These memories are in no specific order, just free-flowing thoughts.

Mam was a pleasant-faced, motherly woman who wore a big white prayer cap over her graying hair. Dat was a kindly man with twinkling eyes, who liked to tease youngsters in a friendly way. I remember the boys and girls being at home yet, and sometimes some of the nieces and nephews would be there to visit, some of them being close to my age.

Mam had a treadle sewing machine, and on it she sewed for me a sunbonnet and a dress like the little plain girls wore of below-the-knee-length. My mommy didn't care that they sometimes put my plain dress on me as soon as I arrived, and changed me back into my town clothes just before she arrived to pick me up. She even got a kick out of it that when I'd be upset about something she did, I'd say to her, "I'm going to tell Mam on you!"

One time when we were all at the dinner table and had our heads bowed to say grace, I peeked, and said, "Barbie doesn't have her head bowed and her eyes closed!" And afterward I said to her, "You must close your eyes and pray." They told me that Dat later told about it to a roomful of company.

A few times I went along to Mam and Dat's church. I was allowed to hold the horse's reins—I thought I was driving the buggy alone. I remember pushing the brake so the horse wouldn't go too fast down a hill. When Dat walked to the singing table, I said out loud, "There's Big Dat!"

When I was 5 years old, my twin brother and sister were born. How excited I was to tell my babysitters. I held up two fingers and said, "Tswae bupplein," like my dad told my to.

I liked to go along down to the cold cellar. It was white-washed, with an arch. It always held goodies. Once it was filled with all kinds of cakes and cookies, big crocks of jam and fruit salad, and even a big container of mixed candy. It was all for one of the girls' weddings and I couldn't eat anything. When they told me that she would be moving

16 miles away and I couldn't see her anymore, I, almost in tears, said to her, "Please don't go."

Dat liked to tease me about the big, life-sized doll I brought along to play with, and threatened to put her into the furnace. To tease him, I purposely sat her in his chair when I'd see him coming in the walk. I also brought along my little green elf man to play with. Dat teased me too, about that, and hung him up on the hook that was used to hang up the gas lamp, saying that he was to catch the flies.

I remember making donuts, applesauce, and pies. Mam always let me lick the beaters and the bowl. I also remember slicing potatoes real thin and putting them on the cook stove to make potato chips. When we made applesauce I got to turn the wooden thing and watch the apples squeeze through the holes. It was the best applesauce ever.

I can remember helping to can. There was a huge kettle in a room off the porch that sat on a fireplace. The jars sat in boiling water and we used special tongs to get them out.

Whenever pies were made we got to take the last of the dough and roll it out and put spices and sugar on it, then roll it up and cut pinwheels. They were really good. The girls made good cinnamon rolls, too.

I remember eating the best pickles ever. I could eat a quart at one sitting. At dinner, if we had chicken, I always got the heart. The girls always had a fit because they wanted it. We also ate marrow bread. It was one of Dat's favorites and mine too.

Barbie and I spent a lot of time under the bridge slopping in the "crick" (as we used to say for creek), looking for the neatest rocks with the best colors to make our rock families. We gave them names and played for hours, just sitting on the big boulders with all the little rock families. Once the horses came galloping up through the meadow and we were running and screaming, trying to get out of their way. We would also go on top of the bridge and drop rocks through the holes.

We used to plait each other's hair. Later the girls had "bobs." I remember the girls ironing their coverings with one of Mam's butter knives. They wanted the creases just so.

I remember when Barbie had her bike accident. She ran into a guy coming down a hill, also on a bicycle. We teased her about there being better ways to meet guys. She had to drink everything through a straw because her mouth was wired shut. She couldn't talk very well and lost weight.

The neighbor boys used to come over to play. One of them dared me to touch the electric fence. I used a long piece of grass, thinking it wouldn't shock me, but it did. Of course he laughed.

Once I tried to help milk the cows. I could never figure out how to sit on that three-legged stool. Dat used to squirt milk at the cats. There were big milk cans that sat in water to cool in the milk house. There was also some sort of strainer the milk was poured through.

I remember going for walks through the meadow. We picked and made a lot of meadow tea. One time I tramped on a thistle and had to have the needles pulled out. I'm sure I also tramped in a few cow patties as we walked through the meadow and waded in the creek.

Once I was drying silverware to help out. I dried one piece at a time, and Mam was pleased because the girls just grabbed a bunch and they were never dry when they put them in the drawer. The silverware had yellow handles on them.

When it was cold outside I remember standing over the heat register holes in the kitchen floor. It warmed you up quickly. Barbie used to stand there and practice her reading lesson.

I remember playing house in the cornstalks when they were harvested in the fall. We also had a little house under the beanpoles and pretended to be the country mouse and the city mouse.

In a cage was a black dog that had puppies. I remember the pen outside at one end of the barn. We used to sneak in and play with them and get them out and put them under the apple tree on the barn hill.

There was a grape arbor out front by the windmill. I remember eating grapes and spitting the shells at each other. When the wind blew, the windmill wheel turned real fast and made a whining noise.

I thought it was really cool to pump water with the hand pump in the kitchen. The water was ice cold.

I can remember walking across the bridge to the mill, and always getting pretzels. The mill was close to the dam and we liked to watch the water rushing down over.

We also walked to Minnie's to use the phone. She was a short roly-poly lady with a big black car. She sometimes brought a message to the farm. Once we were all at the table eating when she came over, and she helped herself to a piece of homemade bread.

One day we went to the Mansion for a funeral. I remember the parlor being dark and a young boy lying there. One boy happened to shoot his brother and it was a sad time.

One evening we all went to the range houses to catch chickens. They were loaded in coops on to a flat-bed wagon. I was told to sit on top to help hold them. The chickens pecked at my behind! It wasn't funny then, but looking back it is. Those heavy horses could trot fast.

Barbie and I often took walks to gather chestnuts. They were really picky. We also gathered and ate little round green edibles called kase bopplers.

One day Dat walked on stilts on the driveway. He seemed so tall—like a giant. I can remember trying to walk on them and couldn't, so I walked on tin cans with a string or baler twine.

I remember playing house in the carriage. I always wanted Dat to be the horse. He used to pull me in the driveway, when he moved it out of the carriage shed.

I remember Good's Store. We often went there. Once Mam bought me a little china bowl with flowers on it and a toothpick holder with a little mouse, for my hope chest. I wanted to be like the farm girls and have a hope chest. I still have these items in my house. The toothpick holder sits on my countertop.

There was also a parlour that was off limits. There was a candy dish filled with candy in there, but it was for the girls' boyfriends.

Mam and I would sit looking through the flower and vegetable magazine looking for the kitten that was hiding in the pictures. I was always excited when I found it.

We went to the spring house to get watercress. I can remember the water being ice cold. I found a rock there that we were sure was petrified wood. Crossing the bridge we would look down and see the water rippling over the rocks.

We spent time playing in the barn among the hay bales looking for kittens and looking down the holes in the floor, at the steers. I was always afraid I'd fall in there with them. It was exciting to watch from up there when the steers were being loaded.

I used to love hunting for eggs and finding the tiny pullet eggs. There was a chicken with no tail named Bobby. There was also a pet pigeon named Squabby, which the dog later made a meal of.

I remember planting corn. The seeds were pink and Mam told me that was because it had stuff on it so the bugs didn't eat them. She made me wash my hands really good. We put three seeds in each hole. I also remember Dat pulling a hand plow to dig up potatoes. I loved walking through the garden with my bare feet. By the end of the summer I could run on the stones in the driveway.

I remember going to pick raspberries and eating a lot of them before we ever got back to the house. Mam made a good soup with cold milk, bread cubes and berries.

One day someone killed some chickens. I can remember how blue their eyelids were and they would flop around after their heads were cut off. I also helped pluck them. Even as I remember this, I'm wrinkling up my nose—I didn't like that smell.

I was always amazed when Dat would light the old gas lamp that hung in the kitchen. It had sock-like cloths (mantles) that would really glow.

Dat had his favorite padded chair that he would sit in to look at his mail. Sometimes he would read aloud out of the Bible and tell stories.

There was a quilting one time and we children played under the quilt and would make the quilt move and all the ladies would holler because they pricked their fingers. Later the girls served glasses of tea and big cookies with icing.

There was a man named Boschty Hoschty. I'm not sure that's really how you spell it, or how he came around. He collected dead chickens for his foxes, and gave us candy corn.

I remember the girls and I trying to get the little pigs away from their mom so we could play with them. We played a lot with the kittens, too, and each had our favorite one.

I remember going to feed the animals in the barn. I'd take apple slices to the horses, and stroke their velvety noses. They would make snickering sounds.

We went boating a lot on the crick. The boat was always tied right at the top of the dam. I was always afraid we'd go over, and of course the girls would always rock the boat. They told me snakes lived in the water and that it was so deep it was over their heads below the dam. One day we went for a ride in the boat and we were close to the shore. The girls were rocking the boat so hard I fell in headfirst. When I came up I was mad because my head was covered in mud and they were laughing. I hadn't swallowed any water but I was terrified that

I'd not be able to get that mud out of my hair. I can remember this like it was yesterday.

We also used to go for picnics on the island up stream. We picked cat-o'-nine tails and pretended we were fairies. The food was always stashed in egg baskets, and we'd have some of those pickles I liked so well. Barbie liked them as well as I did, but Dat sure didn't.

I remember running up to Dat's mother's house. She would be sitting in her kitchen on her armless rocking chair. At first I was afraid of her because she wore dark clothes and I thought she looked like a witch. But when I got to know her better I learned that she was just a friendly grandmother who gave pink lozenges sometimes, or after-dinner mints. They had a dog named Tippy who didn't like children very well—he could snap. They also had a horse named Dolly and we would take turns pumping water with the old long-handled water pump to fill her trough. Later there were white rabbits in the shed beside the barn, and once I got scratched when I held one.

I don't remember much of the old Grandpa who lived there. He walked with a cane and he could make pies. I think he once had a heart attack and was in the hospital for awhile.

That's about it, for the memories of being at my babysitters'. I was thrilled when I was asked to jot them down, for those memories are good ones. Later on, when I no longer regularly went there, I was always excited to go to Mam and Dat's for a Saturday or for a visit. We would always bring some special treat like ice cream or candy.

Like I said in the beginning, I have very fond memories of my time at the babysitters' house. I don't remember working very much, I just remember all the fun we had. If I close my eyes I can imagine I'm a little girl again, reliving the magical moments of childhood on the farm. There are special memories to cherish; such as, the hens in the chicken house clucking as we gathered eggs, the squeak of the old-fashioned iron pump in the kitchen, the sound of the windmill when the wind blew, the purple martins chirping as they flew around their house, the friendly horses and cows in the barn, buggy rides, boat rides, Dat telling stories after the work was done—stories of Indians that made us shiver—stories of mighty men of valour in the Bible. Time goes on, things change, but we can always treasure our good memories of the days that are past.

Barbara said that Teresa was very soft-hearted, especially if a helpless little thing like a kitten or a puppy got hurt, and she would very tenderly care for it. She must have been a very nice girl.

RAINY DAY

Today we had an all day rain—the kind that fills all the cisterns, and raises the waters of the creek bank too full. Mumsy and the girls were sewing, and so I spent the day in the attic, with the music of the rain drumming on the roof in my ears. I sure enjoyed going through the boxes of old letters, books, and magazines. I found an old autograph book of Maria's, which had been given to her when she was 10 years old. Someone who wrote in it used silly, teasing verses, but the one her grandmother wrote was very true and good advice. She wrote:

> Always be honest and good and true,
> Always do what is right to do,
> Always be kind to those you meet;
> These are the things that make a girl sweet.

Maybe that's why Maria has such a sweet personality. (She must have taken her grandmother's good advice to heart.) One day I told her, "You must have been born good." She said, "Oh no, I was born one way and born again another way." She even said she inherited all the bad traits of her worst ancestors. Huh! I know better.

I found quite a few "hidden treasures" up there in the attic, but the best of all was a small journal that Grandmother kept. She has gone on to her reward now, maybe that's why her writings were so interesting to me. Grandfather was a preacher, so they had many church-related duties, and raised a large family besides. Mumsy gave me permission to copy her memories here. She wrote:

We were married on a brisk fall day, but did not start house-keeping until spring when we moved to a 50-acre farm. It was a new experience for us, but we had high hopes. Money was scarce and everyone was poor in those days. That winter Dad went to farm sales and bought horse-drawn machinery, which was cheap. The only new implement he bought was a plow.

I got two cows from my parents—the one was a very good one. So we were disappointed when the cows were tested for TB, and our best cow was condemned. We were happy when later she did pass the retest, though. A few years later she became bloated and appeared to be in the last stage of life. Dad quickly stuck her with his pocket knife, then called the vet. The vet came out, took one look at the cow and said that she is a goner. He said there's no way she can live, being stuck at the wrong place. (Dad had just made a guess as to where to stick her.) But the cow did survive and we had her for many more years.

We bought eight steers to graze on our 3-acre meadow. But three of the steers died—one choked on green apples and the other two bloated. In talking to our neighbor about our bad luck, he said, "Oh, let us rejoice if death stays in the barn, but it doesn't always."

That first summer we had many salesmen, peddlers, gypsies, tramps, and Negroes come to our door. The salesmen were so sorry the former owners had moved away. They'd ask, "Where did they go to?" They probably needed more than we did.

Dad got a nice dog named Rosie. She was such a good watch dog. Great-Grandpa used to walk down to our place early in the morning when it was still dark, and Rosie would hear him and bark when he was still far up the road. Sometimes he tried to walk real softly, but Rosie always heard him and barked.

We were blessed with good rains that first summer and had good crops. We had very nice rows of sugar peas, but very little hull peas. People didn't plant many in those days. We had nice big potatoes and other vegetables and plenty to eat even though we were in hard times. I remember I made an order to Sears, Roebuck and Company, but then Dad's pocketbook was empty and he couldn't buy a money order from the mail carrier. He said to me, "You probably wish you had married someone who is richer." My answer was, "Ach, sie sinn aal orm allaviel." (Everyone is poor just now.) Which was very true!

Dad had worked for a neighboring farmer when he was 21, and at the end of the year that man had no money with which to pay him. When we went to Lancaster for our marriage license and some clothing, we shopped awhile, then went to Watt and Shand for a meal of tomato soup and a little ice cream. We picked up his plain suit last at Hagar's Store. When Dad wanted to pay the $30.00 for it, he was embarrassed to discover that he didn't have quite enough money. I had a little bit left and paid the rest. He felt humiliated, but that's just how it was in those days. We had just enough left for the trolley fare home.

That fall, Dad cut the corn in shocks and we husked corn until about the middle of November. Dad took time off for hunting, for we needed the meat. I don't remember how many pheasants and rabbits he shot, but it was quite a few. I rolled the meat in cracker crumbs and fried it until brown, which made a tasty meal. Deer hunting was almost unheard of in those days.

Dad also bought five heifers and two work horses that fall. The man offering the heifers wanted $20.00 a piece for them. Dad told him he would like to have them, but he doesn't have the money. The man said, "I'll bring them over, then you pay whatever you can." They turned out to be good cows. We bought several more cows and horses on credit.

We had gotten 600 chicks in the spring, so we had pullets to house in the fall. The price of eggs went up to 40¢ a dozen, which wasn't too bad considering that the feed was only 25¢ a bag. We had also set some clucks with duck eggs, which turned out to be not fertile. The following year we had quite a few ducks, turkeys, geese, guineas, etc. We had about everything, except no peacocks or alligators.

Our first daughter was born that winter, on a drizzly Sunday morning. Now we had an altogether different life—we were now "Dad" and "Mam." The doctor kept me in bed for nine days and came every day to check on us. His bill was $15.00 for everything. We were thankful that all was well. She was a good baby and seldom cried, except when strangers wanted to hold her. When she was nearly a year old, I would sit her on the big rocker, tie her so she wouldn't fall off, and gave her toys to play with. Then I'd let our good dog Rosie into the kitchen to watch her while I helped to milk the cows and gather the eggs. Rosie would not allow anyone to come near the baby.

Our second daughter, a fat, healthy baby, was born the following spring. When she was a half year old and sitting on the floor, she began to cough and cough. I thought, "I believe she has a cold," but then a ground cherry popped out of her mouth. Her sister had given it to her.

Around that time, I got the mumps. The doctor said he believes the girls will get fat faces too, but they didn't.

When she was two years old, our oldest was able to help wash dishes by standing on a little bench and she liked it. One day a little

rocking chair came by mail for her, but she didn't forget about helping with the dishes.

That summer our church decided to ordain a minister. Dad was in the lot with older, esteemed men and one deacon said, "Ess iss ken gefor es as ihn dreft." (There is no chance that he will be the one.) But the lot fell to him. We were very cast down, not feeling able to do the work, but instead feeling that we could never be happy and carefree again as we presently were.

The brethren in the church, friends and neighbors, were all very helpful. The mailman put a slip of paper in the mailbox that said, "The whole neighborhood is praying for you."

Now there were more responsibilities, and no more staying at home on Sundays and taking it easy. Travelers came overnight and for meals, and there were weddings, funerals, preparatory services, instruction meetings and communion services.

Dad made the remark that people are very kind to us even though they'd rather have had one of the others. He would often say to me, "If only I'd be more gifted and more able for the work." I told him I think it's more important that we live up to what he does preach instead of wishing to preach better. I always prayed for him for every sermon.

The more duties we had, the more we depended on God's help. We knew He would never load anything on us that He is not willing to help us carry.

Sometimes Dad had to go on trips when I wasn't able to go along. He didn't appreciate going alone anymore than I did staying home. Once when he was in Canada, I wrote him a letter. It was just for him, but he happened to leave it lying in his bedroom at Josiah Weber's. They later sent it to us and wrote that they had passed it around to others to read. They thought it was too good not to show to others.

We had much visitation work to do, and I went along whenever possible. Once when we were on a trip to Indiana and had the two girls along, we found out that there was a polio epidemic going on there. How thankful we were for God's protecting hand in that they stayed healthy.

If any of our people were patients in the hospital, which was ten miles away, we tried to take the time to visit them. If we started off after dinner, it took a half day and we didn't get much work done at home. So, we often went in the evening and started home from the hospital at around 8:30 or 9:00 p.m.

One evening a strong wind and heavy rains came up and blew out our kerosene lanterns on each side of the carriage. Dad tried to relight them, but it kept happening again and again. We were so glad to arrive home safely that night. Another time a thunderstorm was coming as we were on our way home. When it came close we looked for a shelter to drive into. There were two barns on ahead—across the road from each other. The one on the left was a large barn, and the other one was smaller with a roof along the side. We drove under the roof on the right, and were very thankful that we did. A high wind came up and flattened the barn on the left!

Another time, coming home from a funeral, lightning hit close by. We were not shocked but the horse probably was, for he reared and plunged out of control for awhile. At another place, a storm came up while we were visiting. We were nearly home when it started to hail fast. Dad feared he wouldn't be able to control the horse, but the horse just put his head down and was not as scared as we were.

The people in general were very nice and sympathetic. But some favored being more strict and others more lenient. There often seemed to be trouble, threatening conditions and decisions to be made to all work together for the good of the church. Sometimes we were nearly overwhelmed.

Once we had an almost sleepless night. The next day Dad lay on the couch (which he seldom did). I brought in the mail and looked at it, and decided it wouldn't be good to give him one letter of criticism. About three months later a couple from another county came to visit. (It was the man who had written the letter.)

We welcomed them inside in our usual friendly way. After awhile, the man started to say something about the letter he had sent several months ago. Dad thought, "Oh, my, I must have forgotten all about his letter which wouldn't suit him at all." So he thanked him for the letter, saying how we enjoy getting friendly and encouraging letters and that they shall write again! He thanked them for coming and when they were ready to leave, told them to write and come again. After they left, I confessed that I had not given the letter to him because I thought he was too discouraged to read the letter at that time. (He made me promise never to do that again.) The man (now *deceased) was friendly later on. Dad did not lie to the man and I hoped it was not deceiving.*

When our son was born, it was a warm spring evening. Dad said a lot of geese were flying that day, and now a stork yet. When the doctor heard that we wanted to give him the same name he had, he said, "Goodness, you flatter me." The doctor's wife was along and she was so pleased. She was wishing for a baby of her own.

Now my sheets are nearly full, and there would be lots more to write. I want to write yet that we feel to say as we read in 1 Samuel 7:12, "Hitherto hath the Lord helped us." Mountains have been moved, so to speak, with the Lord's help. God has been with us in our work and trials, for He promised never to leave us, and that His grace is sufficient.

~ The End of Grandmother's Journal

I wish there would be more to the journal. Maybe when it gives another rainy day, and I sort through more old boxes, I will find some more of her journal entries. But maybe she got too busy to keep on with journal writing as her family got larger.

On Maria's bureau I found these lines and decided they would probably be an apt description of Grandmother and Grandfather:

A jewel in disguise, forgetting self to serve others.
A nugget of gold in the crucible, to be refined from its dross.
A diamond in the rough being polished to shine as the stars.
A pearl in the oyster, to be delivered from the body of flesh.
A lamp in the dark, dark night,
soon to blaze forth with everlasting light.
A flower in a garden of briars, soon to unfold its treasures . . .
Where the Rose of Sharon blooms.

Garden Blessings

Such bountiful yields our garden and patch have this year. We have new potatoes to dig, big heads of cabbages, ruby red beets, young carrots and very soon our first batch of sweet corn, and then juicy red ripe tomatoes. Mumsy and the girls make the "bestest" meals; I'm trying to learn all I can about meal-making, and hoping to be just as good at cooking, soon. We don't cook mush and tripe as often when we have all these bountiful garden goodies—that will wait until the weather is chilly again.

Grandpap likes his *katza graut* tea with his supper, and we make fresh meadow tea often. Fresh vegetable soup is everyone's favorite too.

Today, as Naomi was zipping back and forth through her kitchen, gathering her ingredients to make rolled molasses cookies, her apron somehow caught on a drawer pull and rrriiippp, the bib was nearly torn from her skirt. She just laughed and tore it off completely and said, "Ach, that old patched thing was ready for the rag bag anyway."

"Rag bag?" I wondered.

"Yes," she said. "It's soon time for the rag man to come around again, with his tired old horse and rickety wagon. He calls out, 'Rags, old gumshoes, old leather, rags,' and gives his measly pennies for whatever we have for him. He used to be a lamplighter before electricity came to the towns."

"The lamps were on high poles, and he would go out every evening and lower the lights with a rope and pulley, fill them with kerosene, light them and raise them into place again for the night. They weren't very bright compared to the electric ones." She said, "He will tell you all about it if you take the rags out to the wagon next time he comes around. He talks to whoever will take the time to listen, and always grumbles a lot about the traffic. Before there were 'horseless carriages,' he says, he would always snooze while driving home, and his horse got him safely home. And he thinks he should be allowed to drive in the middle of the road, because the horses were here before the cars." He sounds like quite an eccentric old character. I hope I'm home when he comes again.

Oh yes, another garden goodie that I forgot to mention is the blueberries. They are starting to ripen, and are they ever delicious! Yum, I can hardly wait for the pies, for I've never tasted one. Susanna says that I've missed half of my life. Yeah well, we had no blueberry bushes on our place, and Dad never bothered to buy any.

Naomi says that next time the ice man comes around she's going to ask Grandpap to buy an extra chunk to chop up for making blueberry ice cream. He comes around several times a week to see if we need another block for our ice box, and uses huge tongs to carry it into the enclosed porch where the ice box sets. We had an ice man, too, back home, and I remember scrambling up on the back of his wagon to try to find little chips of ice to slurp on.

Our winters were almost always cold enough to make thick ice on the ponds. The ice was cut with a saw, into blocks, and stored in buildings called ice houses. The ice was buried in sawdust to preserve it for summertime use. "Mmmm—ice cream made with pure milk, cream, and berries—none better," Naomi says.

Ya well, it's time to quit my random scribblings and go help Barbara in the garden. It's such a beautiful, breezy evening, and we want to go boating when the work is done. Seeing all the fireflies flickering on and off in the trees, and the stars twinkling overhead in the twilight puts me into something akin to ecstasy, or "rhapsodies of splendor sweeping through my soul," as I once

read in a book. When all is quiet and the water peacefully laps against the side of the boat, and the frogs are croaking, then the thrills go up and down our spines, and no one is talking and bantering; the enchantment of the evening has us spellbound.

Heat Wave

Whew! I can't remember that it ever got this warm and muggy in Ohio. Dad and I used to sit on the wooden porch rockers and sip cold lemonade when the work was done. There was almost always a breeze going there. I'm missing him tonight, and the stories he used to tell of when he was a boy, and of his *rumshpringing* days. When he was about 13, an old ornery joker persuaded him to take a chew of his "good" tobacco. Well, he got dreadfully sick, and that was both the first and the last time he tried it. He said that at weddings they used to pass around hand-rolled cigars, also if there was a new baby in the family and company came to see it. I guess they didn't know any better in those days. If you think of the many undernourished and starving children in some cities, it doesn't make sense to use God's good earth to raise tobacco, nor to spend money for it.

We had a table full of company on Sunday after Weberthal Church services. The flies were very pesky, so they appointed me as the "fly-chaser." I used a long-handled homemade swayer, and had to walk back and forth the length of the table, agitating the flies as I went, while the guests were eating.

Mumsy had just chased a whole storm of flies out the door yesterday with her big swayer, calling, *"Mach de daah uch"* (open the door). But they must have all slipped back in whenever the screen door opened, for there's still as many as before.

The girls and I went swimming after the last dishes were washed and put away. Soon Barbara will be an old married lady, and will always have to be prim and proper, and sit with the women, fanning herself. But for now she can still dive into the water, swim underwater to her unsuspecting sister and duck her good and proper.

Time to go indoors before the mosquitoes find me here on the little bridge. There's heat lightning flickering in the sky above the mill. I hope we'll have a storm that will cool off and refresh the whole Conestoga Valley. This weather is hard on man and beast. I just heard of a 17-year-old boy in Groffdale who was working hard in the fields last week and got sick from the heat. A heat stroke I think they called it. He has been in bed ever since, and they're not sure if he's going to recover. That sounds almost like the boy who got overheated from working in the hot sun, then jumped into very cold spring water and was bed-ridden or paralyzed the rest of his life. Whoops, I just heard an *"Eeeeeck, mine friendt!"* whine in my ear, so I'll scoot.

PART THREE

Autumntime

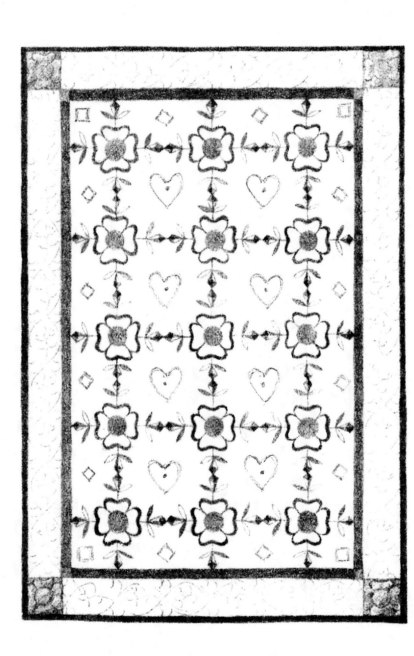

In the Egg Cellar

Some of our evenings are spent in the cool egg cellar. They are evenings of bantering, mirth and hilarity as we clean the eggs we carried in from the chicken house in wire egg baskets. My aunts are gifted with not-so-subtle senses of humor, and once they're in the right mood things can get pretty lively.

Last evening I missed out on it, for I went coon hunting with the boys. I loved that—traipsing after them through the woods and meadowlands, and holding the sack. They got a big one with Patsy's help and it was exciting to watch. Coons love to steal sweet corn, and so are varmints that must be kept from multiplying too much. We had a merry time, and I couldn't help but think of these lines:

> See the merry farmer boys tramp the meadows wide,
> Trudging down a leafy lane, farm dog at their side;
> Bobolink in maple high, trills a note of glee;
> Farmer boys, a gay reply, whistle cheerily.

Barbara has her wedding dress, her second best and her petticoats all sewn already, and is busy canning extra fruits and vegetables for her own home. Susanna whitewashed the woodshed this week, so there won't be as many last minute things to do before the wedding. I helped her stir the fizzling and bubbling lime water mixture and brushed some of it on.

I can hardly wait until November gets here, as I'm to get a new dress, too. But I won't be sewing it myself yet. I'm learning though. I've made two aprons for myself, after practicing on doll clothes for weeks.

Steven and Jonathan caught a huge snapper turtle in the *schwamm*, and brought it up to the barnyard. They teased it by poking sticks toward its mouth. It looked like it had the power to snap them in two. Mumsy's planning to make snapper soup. The boys claim that it's delicious but I doubt that it's better than oyster stew.

Ya well, the girls are carrying the egg baskets into the cellar and I must go help. Cleaning eggs is fun when there's lively bantering and storytelling going on.

APPLE BUTTER TIME

Time keeps moving swiftly onward, much faster than it did when I was a little girl. I'm now in my last year of school, liking it much better than I did the first two weeks, before I got to really know my schoolmates. The girls are friendly and chatty, and we write in each others' autograph books.

Mumsy let me stay home today to help (and watch) the apple butter making. It was a long and interesting day, and now I'm sitting by the dam, enjoying the glorious sunset, in hues of red, purple and pink, while strings of honking geese in V-formation wing their way southward.

The weather was perfect for cooking apple butter. Some of the married children came to help, bringing covered dishes, and so we had a feast of a dinner, starting, of course, with tangy new apple butter on fresh homemade bread. The highlight of the desserts was the ground-cherry pie—another thing I never tasted before coming here. Mumsy's crispy fried chicken remains a family favorite also.

We all helped to snitz apples, then Grandpap built a good fire under the big iron kettle on the tripod, and filled it with apple snitz and cider. The boys and I took turns stirring it with the big wooden stirrer. It took most of the day. Then after the work was

done, we young folks stirred up the fire again and roasted chestnuts while we sat around it telling stories. I believe everyone had their share of friendly visiting and also their share of apple butter to take along home.

Ya well, the golden Indian summer moon is rising up over the treetops, and I'm writing in the dark. Mumsy never says anything anymore about not staying outside in the late evening dampness, for I haven't coughed nor had a pain in my side for ages. I'm sure

I've completely outgrown my consumptive tendencies the doctor talked about. Praise God from whom all blessings flow.

Next there's a corn-husking bee that the *yunge* are looking forward to, then a quilting, and finally the wedding, and then Christmas. There are so many happy occasions when you're part of a big family.

CORN HUSKING

I wasn't allowed to go to the corn husking because only the *rumshpringers* were invited, but Susanna and Naomi told me all about it. Barbara and Maria didn't go—I guess they're both considered to be half-married. Well, not Maria yet, but probably next year. It's kind of sad to think that the girls will be leaving one by one, and the leaves will be taken out of the big kitchen table to make it smaller. Soon I'll be alone with the boys, and then we'll move into the *Daudi haus*. Such is life, I guess.

The evening of the corn husking was a beautiful one, the sun setting in a maze of rose and pink. As soon as darkness fell, a large full moon rose up over the treetops and cast a silvery glow over everything. I walked along the corn-stubble field down to the run, then followed it to the mill. I was wishing I could be at the corn husking, to see and hear everything that transpired. This is what they said it was like: There was a long line of buggies, the horses trotting in the lane one after the other. When everyone was there, the laughing, chattering young people began pairing off for the husking in the moonlit field. Susanna and Naomi both husked with their cousins; so delighted to be chosen by them, I'm sure, as neither of them have boyfriends yet.

They said a few mischievous young boys tried to light a corn shock, but the older boys got it out before the shock was ablaze. That would have lit up the whole field and done damage.

After the work was done, everyone was invited to the house for doughnuts and cider. Afterward a new couple paired off and drove out the lane together, followed by the usual whistles and catcalls that accompany a new match.

I asked Susanna, "Don't you wish it had been you?" Her reply was:

> See the moon is shining bright,
> May I see you home tonight?
> No, the stars are shining, too;
> I can see my own way through.

It goes to show that she hasn't found Mr. Right yet. I hope he finds her, for whoever gets her will be lucky.

QUILTING

The ladies have come and gone, and now Barbara has her last two quilts finished, neatly binded and folded and put in her hope chest ready for her new home. I helped, too, but mostly listened to the interesting chatter. Their tongues flew faster than their needles. We learned who has new babies or beaus or aches and pains. Neighbor Bens were on a journey this past summer, way down to Mexico and British Honduras in Central America, to visit friends. Mrs. Ben talked quite a bit about their trip and I will relate some of it in my journal.

In Mexico, the Russian Mennonites there have concrete walls around their premises. And they saw large, black parrots sitting in the trees. The visitors attended church services there, and

not one person spoke to them before the services, nor did they speak to each other. That's part of their belief, or custom. The preacher wore a flat cap and leather boots. (They, at first, thought a policeman was walking into the church, but it turned out to be the preacher.) All their ministers wear boots, for they take Ephesians 6:15 in a literal sense. They have written sermons for every Sunday of the year, that have been handed down for generations. This they do so they don't get away from the old faith, or doctrines. They were saying that this might seem dry to others, or not giving the Spirit place to rightly divide the word of truth about conditions we face in our time. But, on the other hand, they realize that many groups have gotten away from the old Mennonite faith so far that they themselves complain that they have drifted so far off the foundation into worldliness that they only have the name "Mennonite" anymore. So we don't want to judge each other in how we hold fast to that which we have been taught.

They don't observe "feet washing," nor the holy kiss. The song they sang at their church sounded like the way the Amish sing. Their children don't go to church until they're 12 or 14. Wow! How odd that would seem, never having attended church in my lifetime, yet.

They saw miles and miles of semi-desert, poor-looking huts with thatched roofs, herds of goats and thin-looking Holsteins. In some areas they said it takes 40 acres to support one cow. They saw small adobe houses and huts of sticks and cardboard, with pigs tied in front. The ladies were saying it makes you wonder who the people are that are living the "rich man's life," but on the other hand, some people spend their money on drugs, liquor, tobacco and other lusts of the flesh and worldly amusements, rather than provide a decent home and living for their families.

While they were still in the United States, at one place they stopped, the people said they saw 17 poisonous snakes that spring—rattlesnakes and copperheads!

In British Honduras where Ben's friends live, they have a nice climate—no frost and it's seldom over 100 degrees. About all they need to buy from stores is kerosene, salt, and fabric with which to make their clothes. There is no need for winter coats, caps, scarves, and mittens. The whole year round they can gather bananas, coconuts, pineapples, coco, and mangos.

One girl there had very long braids, almost touching the floor—her hair is too heavy to put it up into a "bob." Whew! It would *ferlate* me to comb that out every day!

They drive small horses there, but they are strong, and pulled the whole wagon load of people through the creek. The waters were swirling around them, and the driver said that if it causes any of them "angst" they can go across on the swinging bridge, high above the water. Several of the girls in the group did.

They mow their yard with a machete, and it looks surprisingly nice. They had coco for supper, which looks like an elephant ear plant, but is their potato substitute and tastes very good. They own hundreds of acres of land, but farm only small patches of it. They plant watermelons, beans, peanuts, upland rice, and vegetables. When the visitors were ready to leave, they were taken to the main road in two teams.

Mrs. Ben said that it seems to be a fairly good place to live, easy to make a living, but they need to find the peace and church unity that eludes them there in their small group. In one sense they live isolated from the rest of the world, and yet, they have their troubles and temptations, too. They have trouble with thieves, and terrorists plague the area. A group of hippies from the United States of America moved into the area, where they raise marijuana drugs and practice nudism at their camp. Oh my, that sounds like an undesirable place to start a church group. Maybe they won't stay there long.

We're having golden, mellow autumn days, with ring-necked pheasants crowing from the fence rows. The grape season is over, the cellar shelves are filled with jars of juice, not to mention all the jars of fruits and vegetables we canned. The frost is on the pumpkin and the fodder's on the shock. Here's a poem that Maria gave me:

> The Lord has fashioned by His might
> The sun's glad rays, the starry night.
> He hath created by His word
> Each tree and flower, each singing bird.
> The mountains by His hand were made;
> The rippling brook and forest glade.
> In all creation far and wide,
> May His name be glorified.

BUTCHERING DAY

Another day off from school, for Mumsy says that learning the tasks of homemaking is more important than book learning at my age. Yesterday Caleb sharpened all the knives, and the girls scrubbed the big iron kettle above the furnace in the washhouse, and washed and scalded the sausage grinder and fastened it to the old sawhorse made especially for the purpose.

Steven, Jonathan and I were the chief "grinder turners." I tried to learn all I could while I watched the rest of the proceedings. First thing this morning a fire was started in the big furnace in the washhouse, which was set up as a butcher shop for a few days. The water had to be scalding hot before they started. Uncle Jacob came on horseback, and Lovina, Abe, and little Amos came on the spring wagon, to help. Butchering day is also doughnut day if we have enough help.

Barbara said she wouldn't have missed it for anything—she needs the experience for when she's on her own. She said she hopes to be able to come back and help us here again next fall. By then she'll be married for nearly a year, believe it or not.

The carcasses were hung up, and later there will be the hams and shoulders to trim, and middlings to square. There's always much jovial bantering and visiting going on as we grind, slice, and salt the meat, and strip the fat for lard. The big hams and shoulders will be hung from the crossbeams in the smokehouse, until they are cured and just the right flavor. Visions of tender, home-cured baked ham with pineapple sauce spooned over it, and savory puddins' over fried cornmeal mush, juicy sausages in gravy, and crisp fried bacon over our breakfast eggs danced in my head as I turned the grinder handle over and over.

Susanna remembered the time when Steven was just a little boy, and mischievously fastened a curled pig's tail to unsuspecting Jacob's backside. There was much laughter and mirth at his expense until he discovered it, and then he threatened to stick Steven's head between his ears if he doesn't behave. The silky pigs' ears are another source of merriment and teasing.

We did get the doughnuts made—that was the best part. The kitchen table was loaded with the sweet, delectable, golden brown, yeasty-smelling temptations. My job was to roll them in sugar (and to snitch a doughnut hole whenever no one was looking). I think everyone that helped went home happy, laden with their favorite parts of the meats, and plenty of doughnuts.

Grandpap said tonight that butchering day reminds him of something that happened in the 1800's, as told by an Amish man in a neighboring community. One morning before daybreak his grandfather had gone to help a neighbor with the butchering. While the farmer finished the morning chores, the grandfather started the fire in the washhouse to heat the water for scalding the hogs.

Suddenly the farmer came running in, all excited and out of breath, crying, "The end of the world is coming! It is here! Just come to the door and see for yourself!"

The storyteller's grandfather rushed to the door and looked out. Imagine his astonishment when he saw that the stars were falling—falling like rain! Some of the people knew they were not ready for the second coming of Christ, so they ran to their neighbors to make wrong things right. They wanted to ask to be forgiven, and to forgive one another. It was a time of tremen-

dous fear and trembling. Butchering day was cancelled and the neighbors went home. But the end did not come that day after all, and the people later learned that there was a scientific explanation for the phenomenon—it was a meteor shower. That is not to say that God did not plan it to call people to repentance, and to get ready to meet their Maker, and to serve Him for the rest of their days.

WEDDING PREPARATIONS

Barbara is hoping that winter weather won't come early this year, not until after the wedding, for we are still busy with fall work and wedding preparations. She's hoping for mostly Indian summer weather for raking all those piles of golden maple leaves, but we take it as it comes. Susanna said that at this time a year ago, they had a genuine blizzard, an old-fashioned one, because it came so early. The drifts were almost as high as the fence posts at some places, but swept bare at others. What if it were like that on her wedding day and no one would be able to come? Let's hope not.

I'm kind of looking forward to when the wedding is over, for then we can all relax, and enjoy the winter weather better. After the wood is split and the stock bedded down, there should be long leisurely evenings for sewing, embroidering of samplers, knitting, and of course, popping corn on the big black kitchen range, and munching on juicy red Stayman Winesap apples.

Barbara and George's intentions of getting married have been published at Weberthal Church and the invitations given, so now there's just the whole house to scrub yet, and the food to prepare. Caleb and his Catherine have been published too—their wedding is to be a week after Barbara and George's.

Losing two children in one winter could be kind of hard on Grandpap and Mumsy, but I guess they're used to it, for they are old pros at seeing their children leaving home—this will be the eighth and ninth ones. They'll both be moving to a neighboring district, yet within easy driving distance with a horse and carriage. That makes it easier to see them go. Some parents have seen their newlywed children travel by covered wagon to Canada, and did not see them again for quite a few years.

Jonathan is sitting on a chair in front of the range with his feet in the bake oven to thaw them out, after hauling manure most of the day.

WEDDING MEMORIES

Both weddings are past now, and there is much to write about. The weather cooperated, though it wasn't quite Indian summer-like, but it wasn't extra cold either, and no snow kept the guests from arriving.

We all had to work hard in the last week before the wedding. To me, it almost seemed like the day would never come. But, finally, the house was spotless and the chairs all set in place in the *sitz stubb* and parlour.

On the morning of the special day, we got up real early and hurriedly got the chores out of the way, then bathed, and donned our new clothes. Soon the guests started to arrive, their horses prancing and pawing as the hostlers held them while the ladies disembarked from the carriages. The hostlers had pieces of chalk to mark the horses on their harnesses and the buggies and carriages, so they could match them again in the evening.

The cooks came early to roast the turkeys, peel the potatoes and make the cabbage slaw. The table waitresses were getting the food and the dishes ready for the busy noon hour.

Barbara couldn't eat much breakfast. She claimed there were butterflies in her stomach, which means she was too excited to eat.

At the doorway the ushers stood to take the people's wraps, and the wedding gifts were handed to the gift receivers. The young people went upstairs, and the older married ones stayed downstairs. Barbara and George were sitting on chairs in the *hous-*

estier stube. She was a beautiful and happy bride, and he looked fine and manly in his new plain-cut suit.

Soon two couples went around carrying trays of *kuchen* and wine (cookies and tiny little glasses of wine). Then one of the young men took the list of the guests' names and called them to their seats. When all were seated, the first preacher rose and began his sermon.

Barbara later said the words made a deep impression on her, for this time the instructions and advice for a Christian marriage and home were for her and George, and that made it especially meaningful. He expounded on the chosen passages in the Bible that portray home life and harmonious living. All the guests were listening intently as the beauty, holiness, and solemnity of marriage was pointed out, and instructions for attaining it were given.

Then, almost before we could realize it, it was time for the bride and groom to stand to be joined together in bonds of holy matrimony. The bishop arose and told the couple to step forward, then asked the age-old questions. Their voices trembled when they gave their "ya," but it was valid, and the bishop clasped his hands over their joined right hands and said the words that joined them for life, then pronounced the blessing.

After the services were over, Barbara and George went upstairs, waiting at the top of the stairs to greet the line of well-wishers who would be coming when the singing stopped, to wish them *gute glick* or the Lord's blessings.

The rest of the day passed in a blur of visiting and singing, until the evening when a sumptuous supper was served, and then there were party games such as Wagon Wheel, Big Four, and others. All too soon it was over, and I was sent to my bed with the echoes of the sounds of the wedding still ringing in my ears.

The next day there was much to do—dishes to pack, furniture to be moved back to its place, and leftovers to take care of. Oh yes,

I forgot to mention what the cellar was like the evening before the wedding. A long table spread with a white tablecloth was put up, ready to be filled with dishes for the tables upstairs. There were at least a dozen frosted cakes on the shelves, huge crocks of pudding ready for the crushed 5th Avenue candy I had prepared, crocks of colorful fruit salad, loaves and loaves of homemade bread, bags of homemade noodles ready to cook with saffron, jars of jelly, cubed cheese and bags of pretzels, washed celery in tubs, jars of chow chow, a gallon jar of mixed candy, and an assortment of cookies.

It sure looked different the day after the wedding. Mumsy sent so many leftovers home with the married children, until I began to be afraid there wouldn't be much left for us. But there was plenty for all, and now I'm glad it's all gone. A week later we went through it again for Caleb and Catherine—the ceremony was much the same, and even many of the same people. But the work fell on Catherine's family that time.

I will miss Caleb a lot—he's so good-looking and always so nice to me. But at least he's not moving far away and I hopefully will get to see him often. But I'll miss Barbara a whole lot more because I'm around her a lot more and closer to her.

The wedding days were both nearly perfect, but I found myself thinking of Dad. He would have enjoyed those wedding days immensely. I said as much to Grandpap. His answer was, "We would not wish him back to this sinful world." True, but we still have *zeitlang* for our dear departed ones.

SERENADING

I'm sitting cozily beside the kitchen range where it's nice and warm. A kettle full of corn meal mush is simmering there, with a "GLUB GLUB" sound every now and then. It's so quiet in here that the "tick-tock tick-tock" of the old-fashioned clock on the shelf sounds quite loud. I'm alone in the kitchen, for Mumsy and the girls were invited to a quilting on this sunny Saturday.

I scrubbed the floor, then made vegetable soup and apple dumplings for dinner. Grandpap praised my cooking, and the boys didn't complain. After dinner Grandpap leaned back in his chair like he does when he's in a storytelling mood, so I asked him about the practice of *gleppering*, or serenading that was popular in Grandfather's day.

He said that at first it was just a seemingly harmless practice—a bit of noise-making to get the young newlywed couple out of bed to give them a treat—but they started getting a little bit rough and rowdy. They'd put pieces of tin on the porch and run back and forth over it, and clang on iron, and use other noisemakers to make a terrible racket. And then they'd not be satisfied with just something to eat—they'd demand money and not leave until they got it. Then they'd head to the nearest tavern and treat everyone to drinks. When people refused to give money they got unruly. At one place they chopped off the grapevines and scattered the buggies over a 20-acre field, and people had a hard time finding their buggies.

Finally the church leaders put a stop to that kind of serenading. Those who took part in it fell under the censure of the church and had to make a confession before the congregation and were reprimanded for their unChristian conduct.

Nowadays there's only light, pleasant serenading at weddings, done in a way that is considered a friendly compliment. Barbara says she thinks the practice should be stopped entirely though, for that is what scared their horse one time.

Ya well, I'd better get busy polishing the lamp chimneys, for Mumsy and the girls will soon be home.

Part Four

Wintertime and the Second Spring

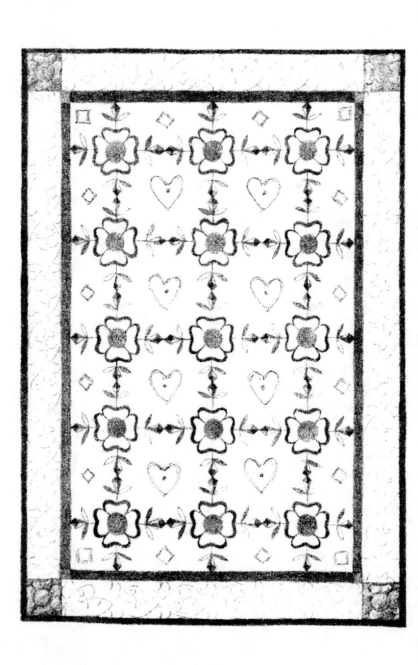

SKATING PARTY

This was one gathering I was allowed to attend, because the party was right here on our farm. The *schwamm* was flooded and frozen smooth as glass, so Susanna and Naomi invited their friends. The weather was clear, cold, and perfect for skating. The boys made a bonfire on the bank for when the skaters need some warmth.

Soon the buggies were turning into our lane, and the ripple-free ice filled with whirling and gliding skaters. They were a merry group—laughing and chattering happily. Steven, Jonathan and I stayed on the outskirts, kind of envious of the fun games they were playing. Soon someone grabbed my hand, and I found myself in the middle of a string of skaters playing crack-the-whip. Jolly laughter rang out as we skimmed over the ice, then sank down by the fire, breathless and panting, to rest.

When everyone had their fill of skating we trudged up to the house for cookies and hot chocolate. So now I got a little taste of *rumshpringing* at a skating party, and it was fun! Naomi said, "If you think that was fun, wait until the Conestoga is frozen over, and you can skate all the way from the dam to the covered bridge—especially on a moonlit night with millions of stars twinkling overhead—and a night when it's not too cold and it's windstill." I hope I get the chance soon.

CHRISTMAS TIME

Yesterday was Christmas Day, and what a lovely day it was, even though it wasn't a white one. The lovely part of it was the family gathering. This morning Mumsy asked me how Dad and I

used to celebrate Christmas. Well, we often went to Aunt Hepsi's for dinner. She would roast a stuffed goose and serve old-fashioned dishes such as stewed prunes and *lep kuchen*, along with *Snitz boi*. My gifts from Dad were often homemade, such as a homemade sled one year, a doll house when I was six, stilts, and a hand-carved farm set.

Grandpap and Mumsy are not so much for giving gifts at Christmastime—instead Valentine's Day is their time to give gifts. Hmmm . . . that's something to look forward to.

We went to church at Zimmerman's Crossing, then went to Jacob's for dinner. It was another big family gathering with bustling ladies, laden tables, gleeful laughter of children, babies crying and cooing, everyone visiting and laughing and talking.

The strange part of the day was the weather. It was so mild we didn't need our coats and shawls—just sweaters. In the afternoon a thunderstorm came up, and the babies became fussier than ever. There was one extra hard clap of thunder, and today we heard that lightning struck a farmhouse within a mile or so from here. A fireball rolled through their kitchen, and something made a dent in an iron kettle in the sink. Luckily it did not start a fire.

Grandpap predicts colder weather again soon, and I'm glad . . . snow would be nice instead of a brown or dull green landscape.

The night before Christmas a wagon load of carolers with two big work horses hitched, came by singing their wonderful, old-fashioned Christmas songs. Then the horses clopped their way out the lane again, on to the next farm. Susanna and Naomi were a part of the jolly, happy bunch, and how I envied them. Here's a verse of one of the songs they sang:

> It came upon a midnight clear,
> That glorious song of old.
> With angels bending near the earth
> To touch their harps of gold.

SISTERS' DAY

All of the sisters and sisters-in-law (I call them mine) were home on this snowy mid-January day. Each brought their own handwork to do, and a covered dish. Some were knitting, some were mending, some hand-sewing, and some were just tending their babies. Steven and Jonathan called it a hen party, and Mumsy called it a *flick 'n Shtrick* party (mend and knit). Luckily, it was Saturday and I could partake of the fun, fellowship and food.

It was so good to see Barbara again—she wasn't at Jacob's gathering, as George's family had them on Christmas Day. They came on the sleigh (for we now have icy, snowy weather again), and came in all cold and rosy-cheeked. She said "the wind stings the toes and bites the nose." She's still the same Barbara, and I'm glad. I was afraid she'd be a prim and proper stranger.

I held the cute *buplein* and rocked them to sleep, played with the toddlers and wiped their noses, read to the older ones and drew pictures for them. After everyone had gone, Grandpap said, "It's just like the old grandparents used to say, 'Glad to see them come and glad to see them go.'"

It's snowing again tonight, or rather sleeting, as I hear it bouncing off the windows. The wire baskets full of eggs must be carried to the cellar through all kinds of weather. Our gab fasts in the cellar aren't quite the same anymore, with Barbara gone. But I still love them dearly.

VALENTINE'S DAY

In August Grandpap said he believes this winter we'll have a "big" snow, meaning a record-breaker, of an old-fashioned blizzard, and now his prediction has come true. Almost four feet of

it we have, with drifts higher than the fences. The wind, with its icy breath whistles around the corners of the house and blows the mounds of snow into the corners. The sun shone brightly again today over all the pristine loveliness, giving it a dazzling brightness. The creek is like a winding, silver ribbon, and the waters at the edge of the dam are frozen into ice sculptures.

We were able to have our valentine "party" in spite of the snow. Lovina, Abe and little Amos were able to come over tonight (on snowshoes) to share in the fun. For two weeks already there has been a big "valentine box" on the stair landing, filling up with presents. Tonight Grandpap, with twinkling eyes, passed them out. He reached into the box and pulled out a little china bird. To amuse little Amos, he put it on top of his head, and moved his scalp, then caught it as it fell. Mumsy said, "*Du net, es fa-brecht.*" (Don't, it will break). Too late—it fell and a piece broke off. Next was a little squeaking puppy for Amos. For me, a 1000-piece puzzle and an apron. The boys got pocket knives and compasses, and the girls fabric for dresses. Then we sang, "Glory Gates," "Never Alone," "Nearing the Port," and "Going Down the Valley." I was reminded of these lines:

> Kindly Heaven smiles above, when there's love at home.
> All the earth is filled with Joy, when there's love at home.
> Sweeter sings the brooklet by, brighter beams the azure sky,
> Oh, there's One who smiles on high, when there's love at home.

I'm working at piecing a quilt this week, and so are Susanna and Naomi. We're racing—trying to see whose will turn out the nicest. Maria takes pity on me and helps me, so I just might win. It's all in fun, though.

We're feeding the birds since the snow came. We are seeing bright, cheery cardinals, chickadees, saucy blue jays, juncos, tufted titmice, and plenty of sparrows. Mumsy encourages the boys to reduce the sparrows' numbers, because of the damage they do in the garden. But the other birds she doesn't allow them to harm, not even in summertime when they are steeling cherries and strawberries. She quotes this rhyme:

> Don't kill the bird! The happy birds,
> That bless the field and grove;
> They sing the sweetest chorus,
> They claim our warmest love.

Already I'm longing for springtime and the cheerful singing of the birds. In the meantime I'll enjoy the blizzards we have, and the sledding, skating and extra time for reading and journal writing. I was reading Mumsy's copybook, and found a piece that describes Mumsy to a T:

Beatitudes for Mothers

1. Blessed is she whose daily tasks are a labor of love; for her willing hands and happy heart translate duty into privilege, and her labor becomes a service to God and all mankind.
2. Blessed is she who opens the door to welcome both stranger and well-loved friend; for gracious hospitality is a test of brotherly love.
3. Blessed is she who mends stockings and toys and a broken heart; for her understanding is a balm to humanity.
4. Blessed is she who scours and scrubs; for well she knows that cleanliness is one expression of godliness.
5. Blessed is she whom children love; for the love of a child is more to be valued than fortune or fame.
6. Blessed is she who sings at her work; for music lightens the heaviest load and brightens the dullest chore.
7. Blessed is she who dusts away doubt and fear and sweeps out the cobwebs of confusion; for her faith will triumph over all adversity.
8. Blessed is she who serves laughter and smiles with every meal; for her buoyancy of spirit is an aid to mental and physical digestion.
9. Blessed is she who preserves the sanctity of a Christian home; for hers is a sacred trust that crowns her dignity.

SLEIGH RIDE

Caleb and Catherine came to visit today on a one-seat sleigh. It looked like such jolly fun! I had never had a sleigh ride in my life so I quickly grabbed my wraps and ran outside. I longingly patted the horse's neck and jingled the sleigh bells, hoping they'd take the hint. Sure enough, Caleb must have seen how much I wanted a ride, for he said, "The horse is still frisky, and wants to run some more, so hop on!" Catherine laughingly gave her place to me, and we were off. We had a new snowfall just yesterday, just right for sleighing, and we whizzed over the frozen snow like magic! The bells jingled merrily and chips of ice flew past our faces and the wind nipped our cheeks.

It was the fastest and most exhilarating ride of my life. I would have liked to go ten miles, but all too soon Caleb turned around and we were flying homeward. Caleb said it would never do to keep me from my work, but I wouldn't have minded at all.

Back again in the cozy kitchen I warmed my hands at the big black range where yet another kettleful of mush was cooking, and I warmed my feet in the bake oven. Soon Barbara and George came, also on a sleigh. We spent the day making noodles, chatting, drinking cider and eating popcorn. It seemed like old times to have Barbara here again, and Catherine is very nice and easy to get to know, too.

It's time to go. The girls are ready to go for a snowy walk in the moonlight, down to the little bridge by the mill, to see the full moon and stars, and to get some exercise.

SAM BRICKER

Grandpap was telling me the story of Sam Bricker and his Beccy, who migrated to Canada in the early 1800's. Beccy's uncle, Christian Eby of Hammer Creek, was one of the instigators of the Canada movement. Sam went over with his brother John and family in covered wagons, before he and Beccy were married, to buy land and build a log cabin home.

After his cabin was finished, Sam went to Muddy Little York to buy a cow for John. There he learned that they had been swindled—the deeds for the land they had built their cabins on were worthless. Sam had red hair, and his ire was aroused. He went immediately to the Head of the Lake and confronted the man who had cheated them in his palatial home. Mr. Beasley, seeing there was no other way, agreed on a new contract.

If Sam and his *friendschaft* could raise $20,000.00 to pay the mortgage, the entire 60,000-acre tract of land would be theirs. Sam was jubilant and set off for Hammer Creek on his Schimmel horse named Menno, to see Christian Eby, and of course his Beccy.

At Hammer Creek they called a meeting to decide what to do. The bishop was minded to refuse their brethren in Canada the request for financial help, and made a speech stating why. But the distressed people back in Canada were besieging the Throne of Grace with fervent prayers, and at the 11th hour the Lord answered their prayers.

Hannes Eby got up and reached for the Bible on the shelf and read aloud Proverbs 19:17—"Whoever has pity on the poor, lends to the Lord, and the Lord will repay him what he has given." Then he said, "It is our Christian duty to assist our friends in distress. If we do our duty in this, the Lord may in His own time and way bless us. I leave the matter to each man's conscience." A new light shone in Sam's eyes when Uncle Christian got up and said, "I pledge $2,500.00." Others followed suit and soon the $20,000.00 was raised.

Sam was overjoyed and rushed back to his Beccy to tell her the wonderful news. They were married and the $20,000.00 was sewn into bags and packed into the *vegle* they would use to travel to Canada.

Meanwhile, back in Canada, a deep gloom had settled over the Mennonites. They packed their wagons, ready to travel home to Pennsylvania in defeat and despair. None of them had any hope that Sam Bricker would get the money.

So when Sam and Beccy arrived in Canada with the *vegle* full of money, the gloom was lifted and it was a cause for great rejoicing. Sam was a hero—Sam and his Beccy and the Schimmel horse.

In the two years that Beccy had waited for Sam to come back from Canada to marry her and take her along back with him, whenever the moon was full she gazed at it, knowing it was the same moon that shone in Canada, and that Sam was thinking of her as they had agreed to do before he left. She thought of all the dangers he faced, such as crossing the Allegheny Mountains, the Susquehanna River, and the mighty Niagara. She loved Sam's Schimmel horse Menno, and pined for them both. What happiness it was when Sam and his Schimmel returned safe and sound, and she was willing to travel with him into the dangers and the privations of the new land. A Mr. Eby from Canada wrote a poem about Sam and Beccy which I'll copy into my journal:

Sam Bricker

From Pennsylfawney Sam Bricker came,
To seek some land it was his aim,
Where he could with his Beccy dear
Set up a home within the year.
    Sam rode off on his Schimmel.

But his Beccy dear Sam left behind
With Uncle Chris who was so kind,
While he searched for a place to dwell,

Chris said in Canada they would do well.
  His Schimmel's name was Menno.

Sam had a brother who also came.
A better home he sought to claim.
John, his family and possessions rode
In their Conestoga where they stowed.
  Sam rode upon his Schimmel.

They crossed Niagra's mighty stream;
The wagon pulled by the swimming team.
John and family tucked inside;
Sam stayed out on the coursing tide,
  Riding on his Schimmel.

They stopped at the Twenty, then on again;
At Coot's paradise they left the main;
Through Beverly swamp they traveled on
'Til civilization was almost gone;
  Sam still upon his Schimmel.

And then at last they saw their prize;
For flowing there before their eyes
The waters of the Grand appeared,
The wagon to its bank they steered.
  Sam stepped down off his Schimmel.

The trees were felled, logs cut to size,
And soon they saw their cabin arise.
It wasn't much but it would do
To keep them that first winter through.
  Sam's Schimmel stood there grazing.

John's house at last was fully built.
Sam had a room with a nice warm quilt.
But Sam decided that he should go
To Muddy York, now Toronto;
    His Schimmel neighed approval.

Could Sam believe what he had heard?
The very idea it seemed absurd;
That Richard Beasley was a dishonest gent;
Was he not a member of parliament?
    His Schimmel could have told him.

Richard Beasley had owned the land,
And Sam had bought it from his hand,
But it was mortgaged to the hilt;
Sam very deeply felt the jilt.
    Sam's Schimmel hadn't liked him.

So Sam took heart, and Sam took spunk;
To the Head of the Lake he was hunting skunk.
His hair was red, his trust had died;
And Sam was after the man who lied.
    His Schimmel moved him faster.

Sam cornered Beasley in his room;
For hours he stalked this man of gloom.
"Peaceful Mennonite" waiting for his prey;
And Sam was prepared to stay all day.
    Poor Menno was forgotten.

Then Beasley decided to face his sin;
To a new contract he would enter in;

If the Mennonite could but the mortgage pay
Their land would be clear, no further delay;
    Real home for Sam's dear Schimmel.

"Twenty thousand dollars!" John said again.
"But look," said Sam, "what we have to gain!
Sixty-thousand acres! Chon, auch my.
Chust think how many a farm we'll buy!"
    Sam's Schimmel neighed approval.

So Sam returned to Hammer Creek
Where Beccy had watched for him week after week,
And quickly to Chris the problem he stated
While Beccy stood by and patiently waited.
    The Schimmel saw her first.

A meeting was called at the Chris Eby home,
Where after the reading of the Holy Tome,
Chris laid out his money to get a fund started
The others all followed before they departed.
    Sam's Schimmel was delighted.

Now a quilt was made ready with pockets for money,
And a vegle was built for the quilt on its journey,
While Beccy and Sam had a great wedding day
Ere they left for their home in Canada far away.
    The Schimmel sure liked Beccy.

And a whole new group joined Sam the next morn,
As a new Pennsylfawney in Canada was born.
But happiest of all, if I heard what he said,

Was Menno who was glad Sam and Beccy were wed;
The Schimmel loved his home.

Ya well, that's the end of the Sam Bricker poem. If I remember right, the stalwart Sam was known to say, "There's chust not many women like my Beccy." They both have been the Canadian Mennonite's heroes for generations.

March Winds

The melancholy, plaintive whistle of the steamer echoes throughout the Weberthal Valley, so springtime must be nearing. Grandpap says we're having more than our share of March winds this year. Today was such a day with the wind howling and whistling around the corners of the house, and whining at the windows. But yesterday was calm and mild; the ground was fit for plowing. Grandpap doesn't have Caleb to help him this year, and so does more of the plowing himself. I think he will have to walk miles behind the walking plow before he's done.

Last night the spring peepers were chorusing, singing their sweet, sad refrain. It's a sound I love to hear, because it's a harbinger of spring. My job these days is gathering dandelion for supper and cleaning it. Mumsy makes it delicious with a bacon and hard-boiled egg dressing.

Little Amos fell off the swing yesterday and broke his collarbone, and so has his arm in a sling. Lovina came over with him yesterday; he hardly even allowed me to hold him, so it must have pained him yet. Mumsy said she once had her collarbone broken, too, but she didn't know it. It happened when she was a school girl—she and another girl were running a three-legged race. They fell in a heap, with the other girl on top of her, with most of the force on her shoulder. The pain was intense, and for several weeks she could hardly stand having as much as anyone bump against her. It was near the last day of school, and when they were planning the school picnic one of her friends became so excited and exuberant about it, that she made a jump of delight and threw her arms around her and gave her a squeeze.

Mumsy said she nearly fainted from the pain and hollered for her to stop it. Her parents were in the ministry and had a lot of church duties and were seldom at home over that time, for it was a busy time of year for them. No one thought of taking her to the doctor to see if anything was broken. She suffered in silence, and eventually it was all healed again. Years later a doctor saw her collarbone, and asked, "What happened to your collarbone?" He said it was broken at one time and healed crookedly. *"Oh well, so gates wones gute gaet."*

It's snowing tonight, big wet flakes that stick to the bushes and trees. I hope we have one last snow that amounts to something, and then springtime!

April Showers

The daffodils and hyacinths are blooming—such sweet, fragrant little treasures they are! I brought in a bouquet of them and put them in the little blue vase. Naomi said it smells like spring in here. We planted the garden yesterday. They are all such good gardeners and know everything there is to know; how deep and how far apart each seed goes.

A robin sweetly sang from the apple tree as we worked, and blossoms from the Summer Rambo apple trees gently floated down on the breeze. Patsy is off to the woodlands these days, chasing bunnies and squirrels. Now, today, we had a gentle spring rain.

April showers bring May flowers,
Shy violets on the lawn.
New green leaves and blossoms sweet;
The robin's cheerful song.

I passed another birthday and now I am 14 years old. How time flies. It's hard to believe that I'm here for a year already, and yet in another way it seems like a lifetime. There are so many wonderful things to learn and do. This morning Naomi said to me, "You seem just exactly like a real sister to me, instead of a niece." That made me happy!

And now for the exciting news—about Susanna! She and I were in the barn milking the cows on Wednesday evening. We had just finished and I was back in a shadowy corner on a hay bale, playing with a kitten, when the barn door opened and one of neighbor Ben's oldest boys stepped inside. He is of *rumshpringing* age, around Susanna's age, I think. Susanna, in her kerchief, was just hanging the three-legged stool on its peg. I don't think Ben noticed me back in the corner as he and Susanna visited. After awhile there was a pause, then I heard Ben clear his throat and nervously say, "Well, Susanna, are you blank?"

She stammered and stuttered a bit as she replied, "Uh, um, wh-why yes, I am."

"Well, would you like to have a date with Levi?" (I don't remember the last name.)

Susanna stuttered and hedged some more (I believe she was dumbfounded) then said, "Give me a few days to think it over. I will let you know by Saturday and then you can let Levi know."

Ben left then, and Susanna started having fits. It was no use asking her any questions—she was in a world of her own. I ran into the house and told Mumsy, and she didn't even seem excited about it. She just smiled knowingly and said that Susanna needs some time alone.

I asked her what Ben meant by, "Are you blank?" She patiently explained it to me like this:

In her grandparents' generation the young folks did a lot more casual dating than they do nowadays. So, when the girls began *rumshpringing*, they bought themselves little "dating books," as they called them. They might have a date with one boy on one Sunday eve, the next Sunday another boy, and so forth. So the boys asked on ahead, and the girl wrote his name in her little book on the date he asked for. That's how it started that they called it "having a date." If her little book was blank on the date he asked for, then, if she thought anything of the boy, she'd write his name in the blank space under that date.

"Nowadays," Mumsy said, "they still use that term, but 'are you blank' now means, are you dating anyone else?" For nowadays, no girl would think of having a date with a boy if she is still seeing someone else. She says it's better that way, for light-hearted dating is not good. Courtship is too weighty a thing to be taken light-heartedly.

On Thursday morning Susanna came downstairs and seemed more like herself again, instead of quiet and withdrawn. She had made her decision—for better or worse, she would give Levi a try. So Naomi was right—she did fetch what she had thrown away—for Levi is the very same boy she was talking about when she had said had she'd rather be an old maid than marry him. Hmmm.

I guess it was kind of hard for her to give up her dreams— that of being a nurse in a hospital some day. I can't understand why she dreamed of such a thing. It's no fun at all to see someone sick and suffering. She must be very noble and unselfish, and I guess that's the very reason she couldn't say no to Levi.

May Flowers

Steven and I went boating on the Conestoga last night. The moon was full and the frogs were croaking as we rowed all the way to the covered bridge, then peacefully floated back down to the dam. I thought of the verse: The flowers appear on the earth, the time of the singing of the birds is come; the voice of the turtle is heard in our land (Songs of Solomon 2:12). Tulips are blooming in lovely colors, yellow buttercups dot the lush green grasses in the meadow, and shy violets hide in the grass.

As I sit here by the little bridge the rushing water comes swiftly down over the dam, making a pleasant murmuring sound as it rushes on its way to the river. The crowing of the ring-necked pheasants is back too, as they strut through the fence rows. That's a sound I love to hear. The mill looks so peaceful when it's not in operation. It wasn't very calm and peaceful a few weeks ago when Jonathan drove into it with the two heavy work horses hitched to the big flat wagon. Suddenly there was a creaking and groaning of timbers, a heaving of the floor, and with a mighty crash the whole thing (the floor) broke down, dumping horses, boy and wagon down into the musty cellar. Jonathan was dazed and shaken, but escaped with only a broken arm. He gets a vacation, at least from the heavy work, but helps more in the house now, and I'm just really getting to know him now. He and Steven are both very nice uncles, but at first when I lived here I got the impression that they wished I were a boy. I think they have accepted me as a "sister" now.

The mill floor has been repaired, and they're all thankful that no one was seriously hurt. Mumsy said, "Praise God from whom all blessings flow."

Susanna gave me a book—an old book containing many helpful "Gems of Thought." I found a verse in it that is also a song.

Alle Christen hoeren gerne
Von dem Reich der Herrlichkeit,

Denn sie wissen schon von ferne,
      Dasz sie ihnen ist bereit;
Aber wenn sie hoeren sagen,
      Dasz mun Christi Kreuz musz tragen,
When mun will sein Yeunger sein,
      O, so shtimmen venig ein.

How true, we all want to hear of the blessings of salvation, but when it comes to self denial and cross bearing, then so few of us are willing.

FAMILY PICNIC

June roses, the sweetest of all flowers, are blooming. Naomi brought a bouquet in from the climber out by the purple martin houses, and their delightful fragrance wafts over to me as I sit here by the window. Today was a perfectly beautiful day for our family picnic; a day of good memories to fill up the last pages of my journal.

The chorus of birdsong greeted the beautiful dawning of the morning, with shimmering dew drops glistening on the grasses and flowers and sparkling on the morning spiderwebs. The buggies and carriages began to arrive midforenoon already, for there were no church services at Weberthal today. It was so good to see Barbara again. I gave her a joyous hug, only then realizing how much I really had missed her.

Steven and Jonathan hitched the two work horses to the big flat wagon, and we all helped carry out the baskets and kettles of food, blankets and tablecloths, and the babies and toddlers. I was hoping we could have a freezer full of strawberry ice cream, but Mumsy said it would be too much work for on a Sunday.

Everyone piled on the wagon, holding on to the little ones, as the horses trotted down the field lane past the field of fragrant new-mown hay and into the cool, shady woods. The woods were so enchanting with the spicy-scented boughs cascading down over the trickling spring, where clear, cold, fresh water flowed into a rock-lined pool surrounded by a bed of mint. All the "big sisters" who hadn't tasted the spring water lately, declared that there's just no water that can compare to the crystal clear and cold spring water, and I believe it.

There were lively, frisky squirrels scampering about, and chipmunks flitted among the roots of the trees. Some of us were even lucky enough to see a little raccoon scamper along a tree branch and into a hole in the tree. It was probably taking a drink of that good spring water, too, before we came.

Caleb started a campfire with twigs the boys gathered, and we spread the blankets in a grassy clearing nearby. Table-cloths were spread on the wagon, and the food arranged on it, so everyone could fill their plates, then sit on the blankets to eat.

We all bowed our heads for a silent grace and thanksgiving before starting. The squirrels didn't respect our time of silence—they kept right on chattering and the birds their twittering. But there was a feeling of deep peace and thanksgiving in our hearts for the blessings and beauty of our surroundings. In spite of tender tuggings toward my life with Dad, my heart was overflowing with joy and thanksgiving for the secure feeling of being part of this big, happy family.

As we ate our good food, I wished I could capture the scene in my memory forever—the feeling of warmth and friendliness, and the affectionate teasing and bantering of my beloved family. It was all so special—the family love and fun and togetherness and visiting.

In the afternoon everyone sat around visiting while I played with the toddlers and held the cute *buplein* to my heart's content. Later, Susanna said, "Let's sing." All were agreed, so she chose this song:

I am looking for a city,
Where the roses never fade.
Here they bloom but for a season
And their beauty's soon decayed.

In this world we have our troubles,
Satan's snares we must evade;
We'll be free from all temptations
Where the roses never fade.